D1274705

EFFECT OF RADIATION ON HUMAN HEREDITY

EFFECT OF RADIATION

ON

HUMAN HEREDITY

Report of a Study Group convened by WHO
together with
Papers presented by Various Members
of the Group

WORLD HEALTH ORGANIZATION

PALAIS DES NATIONS

GENEVA

1957

Authors alone are responsible for the views expressed in this report and the accompanying papers.

PREFACE

In 1956, two committees—one set up by the National Academy of Sciences of the United States of America and the other by the Medical Research Council of Great Britain—reported on the effects of ionizing radiation on man. Although difficult to compare in detail, these reports come to remarkably similar conclusions as to the probable effects on the descendants of populations exposed to increased amounts of such radiations. The emphasis in both these reports was, however, on trying to set some quantitative limits to the potential risks in the light of existing knowledge rather than on attempting to assess the long-term dangers.

WHO's purpose in convening the Study Group on the Effect of Radiation on Human Heredity, whose report is presented here, was essentially twofold: The first aim was to obtain the opinions also of authorities on genetics from countries other than those whose national committees have already stated their views. The second was to hear the opinions of a number of experts on an aspect relatively lightly touched upon in the national reports—namely, the lines of research which should be followed, in the light of present knowledge, to increase our understanding of the genetic effects of ionizing radiations on man.

In addition to the formal report of the Group, the papers presented by various members have been reproduced. It should be emphasized, however, that while the Group's report is intended to represent the views of all the participants, the opinions expressed in the individual papers are those of the authors and do not necessarily represent the views of the Group as a whole.

CONTENTS

PART I

REPORT OF STUDY GROUP

REPORT OF STUDY GROUP ON THE EFFECT OF RADIATION ON HUMAN HEREDITY

The Study Group on the Effect of Radiation on Human Heredity met, by courtesy of the Rector of the University of Copenhagen, in the Council Room of the University, from 7 to 11 August 1956. The agenda adopted was intended to permit exploration of the views of the members of the Group on the theoretical and practical difficulties in closing present gaps in knowledge. The procedure followed was for a number of members to open discussions either by short statements or by the presentation of invited papers. The opportunity was also taken to discuss a number of subjects not formally introduced.

The proceedings were opened by Dr P. Dorolle, Deputy Director-General of the World Health Organization, and the Group elected Dr A. Hollaender as Chairman.

1. Introduction

Man's most precious trust is his genetic heritage, upon which must depend the health and orderly development of future generations. The Group is of the opinion that the well-being of descendants of the present generation is threatened by developments in the use of nuclear energy and of sources of radiation. Both of these developments are inevitable and they should contribute much to man's social and cultural development. It would seem therefore that some risk must be accepted, but if the dangers are to be minimized every possible step must be taken to reduce the exposure of man and to understand the effects of exposure. Only in the light of more knowledge can decisions be taken to define more accurately the maximum amount of exposure which may be accepted by individuals and populations without risk of serious harm.

Radiation has been demonstrated to be one of the agents which produces mutation in a wide range of organisms from bacteria to mammals. The Group is agreed that additional mutation produced in man will be harmful to individuals and to their descendants. While there may be inherent and environmental mechanisms which modify the impact of these mutations over periods of many generations, the effectiveness of such mechanisms in man is not known. In essence then, all man-made radiation must be regarded as harmful to man from the genetic point of view.

In recent years, considerable quantitative knowledge has been accumulated on the basic mechanisms of genetics. There are strong grounds for believing that most genetic effects are very closely additive so that a small amount of radiation received by each of a large number of individuals can do an appreciable amount of damage to the population as a whole. There are, however, many gaps in knowledge particularly concerning these effects in man. These gaps will only be closed after a great expansion of general and *ad hoc* research in genetics and other fields of biology.

The Group has received the following resolution passed by the First International Congress of Human Genetics in Copenhagen, and it notes and agrees (while at the same time noting that WHO's work is only concerned with the peaceful use of atomic energy) that:

"The damage produced by ionizing radiation on the hereditary material is real and should be taken seriously into consideration in both the peaceful and military uses of nuclear energy as well as in all medical, commercial and industrial practices in which X-rays or other ionizing radiation is emitted. It is recommended that the investigation of the amount and type of damage and of related genetic questions, be greatly extended and intensified with a view to safe-guarding the well-being of future generations."

The Group agrees with the memorandum, entitled "Human and Medical Genetics", which was submitted in 1955 by the Government of Denmark to the World Health Organization.[1]

This Group takes note of the report of the National Academy of Sciences of the United States of America[2] and that of the Medical Research Council of Great Britain.[3] It is not intended to reproduce any of the material in these reports, but the Group notes the substantial similarity of the findings and recommendations of these reports and is in essential agreement with them.

2. Natural and Man-made Sources of Ionizing Radiation

The present sources of ionizing radiations of interest for the treatment of problems related to the genetic effects in man include the following:

Natural sources

1. Cosmic radiation.

2. Naturally occurring amounts of radium, thorium and potassium in the earth's crust.

3. Content of natural radioactive elements in living tissues.

---

[1] *Off. Rec. Wld Hlth Org.*, 68, 147

[2] United States of America, National Academy of Sciences (1956) *The biological effects of atomic radiation*, Washington, D.C.

[3] Great Britain, Medical Research Council (1956) *The hazards to man of nuclear and allied radiations*, London

Man-made sources

4. Radioactive material and technical arrangements producing ionizing radiation (such as X-ray tubes and other particle accelerators, nuclear reactors, etc.) used in education, science, medicine, industry and commerce.

5. Sources used by the population for other purposes than those mentioned in 4 (radioactive luminous compounds on watches and other articles for common use, television sets, etc.), although such sources are much less significant than those mentioned in 4 and 6. It is important, however, that their existence be recognized.

6. Artificial radioactive elements distributed by man in nature.

Information as to the contributions to the doses received by individuals and by large population groups from the various sources listed above is summarized in Professor R. M. Sievert's paper (see page 63), from which it is obvious that as regards the average dose to the gonads the most important contributions are at present those from the natural radiation (normal level: between 2 and 5 r per individual in 30 years) and from the radiation received by patients undergoing medical X-ray examination (probable average: between 1 and 3 r per individual in 30 years). If therapeutic exposures are also considered, the "total" exposure to a population might be greater. It is, however, difficult to get sound data for estimating how much exposure is received in therapeutic exposures to persons before the age at which procreation may be expected to be ended.

It may be noted that at the present time the highest dose to the gonads caused by natural radiation in areas with a large population seems to exist in parts of Travancore, India, on ground containing monazite sand (possibly of the order of between 10 and 20 r per individual in 30 years).

3. Importance of Recording Radiation Exposure in Individuals and Populations

From a genetic point of view the total accumulated dose is the important one and for this reason the measurement of exposure to ionizing radiations is an essential preliminary to attempts to relate dosage received to effects in man. For such measurements to be useful, the information must be recorded systematically. Unless the information is available in the form of the dose received by individuals, records of exposure would be unsuitable for many purposes and therefore some system of registration is essential. The effect of recording would almost certainly be to cut down the exposures given in medical diagnosis and treatment, since it would impress radiologists and technicians with the magnitude of such exposures. In one hospital where such recording was started there has been a 30% reduction in the total exposure of the staff. Doubtless a similar system of recording in diagnostic practice would reduce the exposure to the patients. This in itself would be a sufficient justification for introducing the procedure. It seems likely that the two national reports will already have done much to overcome the hesitation to record the dose on the part of those who would be concerned in making such records, but that a recommendation from this Group would also be helpful.

The Group is conscious that the adoption of any system of recording dosage will give rise to difficulties because it will increase the burden of work of radiologists and their staffs. Nevertheless, they feel that the importance of these procedures is such, and is so well recognized by radiologists, that both those in charge of radiological departments and other physicians who use X-rays will be co-operative.

Whatever system is adopted should take into account three desirable requirements:

1.   That the individual will not, through lack of information, accumulate excessive exposure.

2.   That information becomes available as to how much exposure to the gonads is received at each age in individuals and on an average per head of population.

3.   That it should be possible to recognize the amount of exposure received by the parents of a given child. (Eventually, the information would be available for several generations.) This information is particularly valuable for purposes of genetic analysis.

The Group suspects that exposures in some industries and in scientific work are unnecessarily high. Exposures from these sources should be recorded in such a way that the dosage received can be related in individuals and populations to that received from other sources.

It seems unlikely that all countries would favour, or indeed would be able to introduce, the same standards of registration. Although it is expected that recommendations on mechanisms of recording will shortly be available from the International Commission on Radiological Protection, there should not be any delay in improving the standard of recording of exposures.

Whatever procedures of recording and registration are adopted will entail a large expenditure of money and effort. The need, however, is urgent. Further, the present is the appropriate time to initiate such procedures, since the introduction of atomic energy for industrial use and the extension of the use of radiation tools in biology and medicine make it possible to start with such procedures at an early stage of a period of rapid development.

4. Research

General

Additions to the understanding of the effects of radiation in man come from a very wide field of research. It is impossible to forecast what work in biology or genetics will contribute information relative to the problems. Accordingly, the Group is strongly of the opinion not only that as much experimental work as possible should be done on radiation effects on suitable organisms and such controlled observation studies as offer in man, but that there should be an intensification of all human and experimental genetic research. The Group feels that there should be the closest possible collaboration between those working in the experimental and human fields: their work is complementary. Each should be stimulating the other's research projects. This need for intensification of research in man and in other organisms raises problems of finance and of shortages of trained research workers. Both these difficulties are likely to be intensified if new areas of work, such as that on tissue cultures, chemical mutagenesis, serology, biochemical genetics and epidemiological problems of genetic disease, are to develop as rapidly as is desirable. The problem of manpower shortages, in regard to both biologists and physicians, tends to be perpetuated by lack of career opportunity for those working on genetics. There is also an insufficient number of institutions where an adequate training in genetics, particularly in human genetics, can be given.

It is possible that the results of much effort in these fields will prove disappointing. Nevertheless, research workers and those supporting their work must have the courage to face the possibilities of such disappointments and still go forward.

The developments of nuclear energy would never have been made unless enormous risks of failure had been accepted. These innovations have extremely important implications among which the possible effects on man's genetic composition are outstanding. If there is to be a climate of public opinion favourable to the development of nuclear energy, the peoples must be assured that investigations essential for their future health and welfare and that of their children will be undertaken on an adequate scale. This will require recognition by governments that very substantial financial provision must be made for genetic and other biological investigations essential to an understanding of the effects of radiation on man. Biological research in the past has suffered severely from lack of funds.

Specific

The Group does not feel that it should attempt to recommend specific research projects. Nevertheless, it seems desirable to recognize the larger gaps in knowledge as they appear at the present time. Among the fields in which the need for further work is urgent, if the genetic hazards of the irradiation of human populations are to be understood, the following appear outstanding. It should be emphasized that the rapid developments in genetics and other sciences must determine that recommendations for lines of research should only be accepted as tentative and should be revised periodically.

(*a*) *Further study of spontaneous and artificially induced mutation.* There is need for further study of the number and kinds of mutations produced by various doses and types of irradiation applied at different stages of the life-cycle under a variety of conditions and utilizing different kinds of organisms. The relatively limited opportunities to study irradiated human beings and their offspring should be exploited to the fullest extent possible. The appreciation of radiation-produced mutations is intimately related to a similar extension of knowledge concerning mutations that appear to arise spontaneously or as the result of the action of chemicals and of physical agents other than ionizing radiation.

(*b*) *Mutational component in the somatic changes produced by radiation and other means.* The role of changes in the hereditary material of somatic cells in the genesis of leukaemia, in other forms of neoplasms, and in alterations in the life-span is at present a controversial field which needs clarification. The effects of low doses of radiation, including those from radioisotopes, require special study. An important method of attack on this problem is opened by recent developments in tissue-culture techniques.

(*c*) *Means of protection against mutagenic agents.* The pioneer studies which indicate the possibility that the production of radiation-induced mutations can be modified by various means have important implications for man and require extension in many directions.

(*d*) *Development of new and improved techniques for the identification of mutants.* Efforts directed at developing more exact methods for the recognition of mutant individuals, and the distinction between the latter and phenocopies, should be intensified. It is important to prosecute studies of the frequency of a wide range of types of mutations, including those with extremely small effects, recognizable only through special statistical or breeding techniques.

(*e*) *Manner of gene action.* The phenomena of dominance, synergism and other forms of gene interaction, the multiple effects of a single gene and the role of environmental factors in the determination of traits require a great deal of elucidation, since they are highly important in appraising the effects of radiations. They should be studied both in man and in other organisms. In this connexion, the prospects raised by the rapid advances being made on human biochemical specificities are of particular interest.

(*f*) *Selective factors in populations, with particular reference to the special conditions in man.* Very little is known concerning the detailed effects of natural selection on the frequency of specific genes, constellations of genes, or cytological alterations. Such information is basic to attempts to understand the genetic composition of present and past human communities and to predict future trends consequent upon changes in radiation levels, medical practices, and social and economic conditions. These gaps in knowledge can in part be filled by the collection of relevant demographic and experimental data.

(*g*) *Patterns of mating in human populations and their genetic implications.* A standard type of information always required in understanding the genetic composition of human populations and the effect on it of various amounts of radiation is the recording and interpretation of data on the consequences of inbreeding, assortative mating, geographical and cultural isolation and random genetic fluctuations.

(*h*) *Twin studies in man.* These are recognized as being helpful in understanding many problems of human heredity. Such studies have already been extensively used, but could be advanced by standardized registration of twins in various countries. They give useful information concerning the relative importance of hereditary and environmental influences.

(*i*) *Determination of the frequency of diseases with a significant genetic component, with particular reference to their epidemiology.* This is fundamental for investigations on the significance of mutation as a cause of disease in man. In this connexion central registration of human inbreeding, hereditary disease and variation is of the utmost importance. It is also of importance to know the number of people who, on account of hereditary lesions, have to be treated in hospitals or institutions or given social aid.

(*j*) *Study of populations of special genetic interest.* Important information is to be obtained from the study of relatively stable, primitive communities, long isolated by geography or culture. Studies of this type require for their execution teams of persons from a variety of disciplines, such as cultural anthropologists, physicians and geneticists. It should be emphasized that the understanding of the genetic structure of contemporary populations will be greatly aided through these studies, which should be maintained continuously over a considerable period of time. The opportunity for these studies diminishes with each passing year. Among special communities to be studied are those receiving unusually large amounts of radiation, those in which the degree of inbreeding has long been very high or low, and those in which special conditions of selection have prevailed. In some investigations radiation physicists would be essential members of the teams.

(*k*) *Genetic mapping of human chromosomes.* This is a highly specialized field in which encouraging advances are now being made. Among the possibilities to be exploited is the use of such data to aid in the identification of independently occurring mutant genes and in the study of chromosome rearrangements.

(*l*) *Cytochemistry and human cytology.* Direct cytological observations should be conducted both on normal individuals and on those with suspected chromosomal abnormalities. Material from the individuals themselves as well as mutant cells of tissue cultures may be used in such work. Basic information concerning the ultra-microscopic structure and chemical composition of the hereditary material, and the manner in which this is altered by irradiation and other mutagens, is essential and should include information on lower organisms as well as man. The new developments in biochemistry, the emerging immunobiochemical investigation of tissue proteins, bone-marrow and other tissues, the metabolic investigations which may elucidate both physical and mental pathology, the new developments in electronmicroscopy which advanced our knowledge of the structure of human sperm all indicate the development of new tools for the study of human genetics.

(*m*) *Development of further statistical methods.* New mathematical methods have continually to be developed to deal analytically with problems which arise as the result of researches in human and in experimental population genetics. This is particularly so in relation to observations on the genetic structure of and intensity of selection in populations with regard both to traits due to single gene and those due to multiple gene effects. Special techniques requiring electronic computers will also be required for analysing data on genetic linkage in man.

5. Some Conclusions

(*a*) The Group is of the opinion that there are too few institutions or large university departments devoted to general genetics and even fewer concerned with human genetics. It recommends the establishment of such institutions and departments and suggests that there could be no one ideal pattern. One of the benefits of such institutions would be to accustom people of different scientific disciplines having implications for genetics to work together. Physicians, general biologists, geneticists, biochemists, cytologists, serologists and statisticians are examples of the kind of workers who may be needed. When such institutions are concerned with human genetics their location should have regard to the adequacy of existing medical services, to the kind and size of human populations available for field studies and to the adequacy of background vital statistics and general demographic information on the population concerned. For many purposes a population of about two million is optimal, particularly for intensive epidemiological investigations. Such institutions, in addition to their research functions, could eventually serve as centres of elementary and advanced training in genetics.

(*b*) Such research departments and institutions should contribute much to teaching in general and human genetics. Medical undergraduates should all receive training in genetics and the teaching should be co-ordinated with that in radiology and in the use of radioactive substances in medicine, so that the genetic hazards of diagnostic and therapeutic procedures are thoroughly understood. Medical men training as radiologists should have specific, more advanced instruction in genetics. Health physicists, radiological physicists and radiological technicians should also receive instruction in genetics as part of their technical training.

It seems essential that instruction in genetics should be given to all scientists, particularly those whose work is likely to involve the use of radiation and radioactive materials in research. The principles of human genetics could with advantage be conveyed to those training in the social sciences by means of formal instruction. Finally, the Group is of the opinion that public education in genetics should be more common and adequate than it is at present.

(*c*) In the future it would be necessary from the point of view of preventive medicine and genetic hygiene to register serious hereditary diseases and defects in various populations or countries in the same way as, for instance, epidemic diseases. For that purpose, genetic-hygiene ascertainment or registration will be an indispensable and necessary step. The recording of hereditary diseases and defects in various countries and regions is to be highly recommended.

(*d*) In many countries there are very few biologists or physicians properly trained in genetics. This situation will only be solved by producing more career opportunities in genetics, but may be alleviated by granting fellowships or subsidizing training at approved institutions in countries which can offer training facilities. It is possible, also, that advice and technical assistance could be given in connexion with research projects in countries with insufficient resources in trained manpower to carry them out.

(*e*) It might be possible for a United Nations Agency to assist on request in administration or supervision of studies of specific populations over a period of years or by strengthening a research team or by giving advice on organization.

(*f*) In the past, United Nations Agencies have done useful service in contributing to the collection and standardization of vital and health statistics. It is recommended that such agencies continue their efforts and stimulate the efforts of others in the collection and publication of specific data such as fertility, consanguineous marriages and parental ages, which are so essential as background information in many studies in human biology.

(g) The Group wishes to call attention to the evidence that damage to body tissues produced by radiation after relatively small doses is, at least in part, mediated through effects on genes and chromosomes. There is also some evidence that the life-span may be reduced in mammals even by relatively small doses. *Ad hoc* investigations are urgently needed.

(h) The Group is particularly impressed with the genetic hazards of man-made radiation from sources used in medicine, industry, commerce and experimental science, etc. Both as an approach to control and as providing basic background information for relating quantitatively radiation exposure and effects on man, it is essential that methods be found of recording exposures to individuals and populations, however difficult this may prove.

There is reason to believe that radiation exposure can be much reduced; therefore, those in charge of sources of ionizing radiations should always ensure that there is adequate justification for exposing individuals to doses however small. On account of the danger to offspring resulting from irradiation of the gonads by X-rays, consideration should be given to determining what efficient means of shielding the gonads could be devised and brought into general use. In addition, in every exposure, the X-ray beam ought as far as practicable to be directed so that a minimum of radiation reaches the gonads.

Annex

LIST OF PARTICIPANTS

Members:

Dr T. C. Carter, MRC Radiobiological Research Unit, Atomic Energy Research Establishment, Harwell, Berks, England

Dr W. M. Court Brown, MRC Group for Research into the General Effects of Radiation, Radiotherapy Department, Western General Hospital, Edinburgh, Scotland

Dr S. Emerson, Biology Branch, Division of Biology and Medicine, US Atomic Energy Commission, Washington, D.C., USA

Dr N. Freire-Maia, Laboratory of Genetics, University of Paraná, Curitiba, Paraná, Brazil

Dr A. R. Gopal-Ayengar, Biology Division, Department of Atomic Energy, Indian Cancer Research Centre, Bombay, India

Dr A. Hollaender, Biology Division, Oak Ridge National Laboratory, Oak Ridge, Tenn., USA (*Chairman*)

Mr G. H. Josie, Research and Statistics Division, Department of National Health and Welfare, Ottawa, Canada

Dr S. Kaae, Finseninstitutet og Radiumstationen, Copenhagen, Denmark

Professor T. Kemp, Universitetets Arvebiologiske Institut, Copenhagen, Denmark

Dr J. Lejeune, Centre National de la Recherche scientifique, Paris, France

Professor H. J. Muller, Department of Zoology, Indiana University, Bloomington, Ind., USA

Dr J. V. Neel, Department of Human Genetics, University of Michigan Medical School, Ann Arbor, Mich., USA

Dr H. B. Newcombe, Biology Branch, Atomic Energy of Canada Limited, Chalk River, Ont., Canada

Professor L. S. Penrose, The Galton Laboratory, University College, London, England

Professor R. M. Sievert, Institute of Radiophysics, Karolinska Hospital, Stockholm, Sweden

Dr C. A. B. Smith, The Galton Laboratory, University College, London, England

Professor A. C. Stevenson, Department of Social and Preventive Medicine, The Queen's University of Belfast, Institute of Clinical Science, Belfast, Northern Ireland (*Rapporteur*)

Professor O. Freiherr von Verschuer, Institut für Humangenetik der Universität Münster, Münster, Germany

Dr Bruce Wallace, Biological Laboratory, Cold Spring Harbor, Long Island, N.Y., USA

Professor M. Westergaard, Universitetets Genetiske Institut, Copenhagen, Denmark

Observers:

Dr R. K. Appleyard, Acting Secretary, Scientific Committee on the Effects of Atomic Radiation, United Nations, New York, USA

Dr R. A. Silow, Specialist in Atomic Energy, Agricultural Institutions and Services Branch, Agriculture Division, FAO, Rome, Italy

Dr R. L. Zwemer, Chief, Division of International Co-operation for Scientific Research, Department of Natural Sciences, UNESCO, Paris, France

Secretariat:

Dr P. Dorolle, Deputy Director-General, WHO

Dr M. Pizzi, Chief, Epidemiological Information and Morbidity Statistics Section, WHO

Dr I. S. Eve, Medical Officer in charge of Questions dealing with Atomic Energy and Health, WHO

PART II

PAPERS PRESENTED AT STUDY GROUP

DAMAGE FROM POINT MUTATIONS IN RELATION TO RADIATION DOSE AND BIOLOGICAL CONDITIONS *

H. J. MULLER

Distinguished Service Professor, Department of Zoology,
Indiana University, Bloomington, Ind., USA

Accumulation

A topic which the writer has been requested to discuss in this paper is that of the accumulation of point mutations following repeated irradiation. An accurately additive accumulation in the germ cells throughout life has as its necessary and sufficient conditions (*a*) that the induced mutations are stable, i.e., not subject to repair, (*b*) that there is no important amount of intercellular selection to alter the relative frequencies of the mutant and non-mutant cells within a given individual during his lifetime, and (*c*) that radiation given at one time does not by some long-term after-effect influence the mutagenicity of cells irradiated at a later period. These questions will be considered in turn.

(*a*) Changes of a point-mutational nature induced by radiation have not shown, as a class, unusual instability as compared with those arising spontaneously. Although the possibility is not excluded that there may be a relatively short period, of the order of one or a few cell cycles, before a mutation becomes fully completed and permanent (as in the work of D. Lewis [22] on *Oenothera*), this circumstance would not in ordinary cases affect the accumulation process.

(*b*) As for intercellular selection, except for the special case of drastic lethals arising in the X chromosome of a male, which have been shown in a series of experiments with *Drosophila* (by Kossikov,[19] Shapiro,[57] Serebrovskaya & Shapiro[56], to be subject to selective elimination in spermatogonia, there is no reason to expect point mutations of the usual "recessive" sort, appearing heterozygously, to influence the multiplication or survival of immature germ cells appreciably. That mature germ cells are not thus influenced was shown long ago by Muller & Settles.[41] The most pertinent evidence on this point as regards immature germ cells, in an organism related to

---

* This paper is a considerably modified version of that presented at the Study Group on the Effect of Radiation on Human Heredity.

man, is given by experiments carried out by Russell [53, 54] in mice to test this very question.   The failure of the mutation rate to decline in groups of offspring derived from spermatozoa ejaculated at increasing intervals after spermatogonial irradiation, shows both the absence of germinal selection against the mutant cells (point *b*) and the essential permanence of the mutant genes (point *a*).

(*c*) Direct tests of the accuracy of accumulation of lethals induced in *Drosophila* spermatozoa have been made by comparing their frequency at a given total dose after one treatment concentrated into a short time with that after a divided treatment of the same intensity and after a protracted treatment delivered at a low dose rate.   It was found that the frequency depended on the total dose regardless of its distribution in time.   When the diverse experiments of this kind carried out by different investigators (see review by Muller[35] (p. 478), citing work of Patterson, Timoféeff-Ressovsky, Ray-Chaudhuri, Makhijani, Stern and others) are all taken into consideration together, it is found that the time-intensity relation was varied over a range of about 300 000 times without influencing the frequency of the mutations produced.   Thus, a dose delivered in divided or protracted form over a period of a month was as effective as one of the same total amount given in a few minutes.   Tests have also been carried out, by Kerkis,[16] by Timoféeff-Ressovsky,[64] and recently by Oster,[46] that showed an additive relation when irradiation was given successively at two widely separated stages, to the immature and mature male germ cells respectively.

The reservation must be made that mutations not of the point variety, that is, those involving gross structural changes of chromosomes, which result from a combination of two or more independently produced chromosome breaks (Muller[28, 29]), do, as expected, show an increase in frequency when the radiation is delivered in more concentrated form, provided union of the broken ends of the chromosomes can occur to an appreciable extent during the time of the longer treatment.   This condition does not hold in mature spermatozoa, the type of cell used for most of the timing experiments mentioned above, for union of broken ends cannot occur during this stage (Muller[29]), but it does hold in other germ cells, in which, therefore, more lethals of the structural type result from concentrated than from very protracted or divided treatments (Herskowitz & Abrahamson[11]).   In the experiments cited in the preceding paragraph in which both immature and mature male germ cells were used, this matter was not put to the test, since the intervals between irradiations were long enough to avoid interactions between the effects of different exposures.

On the other hand, in gonial cells, which allow union of broken ends during treatment, relatively few of the mutations are of the "structural" type anyway.   Moreover, low doses or dose-rates, such as those ordinarily encountered in human occupational exposures, produce relatively few structural changes as compared with point mutations even in the cells (spermatids and spermatozoa) most susceptible to their production, and produce still fewer in gonia. It must further be noted that at these low doses or dose-rates the rare structural changes which do occur must in most cases have had both or all of their constituent breaks arising as effects of the same fast particle. The frequency of these changes would therefore, in such cases, be independent of the time distribution of the irradiation. For these reasons, conditions would seldom be encountered, except in oocytes, that resulted in over-all frequencies of mutations (counting, together, both those of a point and those of a grosser nature) differing perceptibly from those expected on an additive relation to the radiation dose. And when point mutations only were considered, the relation would be accurately additive.

Linear Relation to Dose

Another expression of this additive relation, in the case of point mutations, is shown by the linear dependence of their frequency on the radiation dose. That lethals induced in *Drosophila* spermatozoa do vary in frequency in this way has been abundantly shown for moderate and low doses, at which most of them are point mutations, in a great array of investigations, beginning with those of Hanson & Heys[10] and of Oliver[44] and proceeding through many others to those of Uphoff & Stern,[67] which brought the dose down to 50 and 25 roentgens (r). In experiments involving a lesser range of dose applied to spermatozoa of *Drosophila*, visible, non-lethal mutations, which include fewer structural changes than lethals, were found by Timoféeff-Ressovsky to show a linear relation to dose, and a linear relation for them was likewise found by our group at Indiana University when appreciable structural changes were excluded by cytological examination. Russell has also found a linear relation for visible mutations resulting from the irradiation of the spermatogonia of mice with moderate doses. A linear relation for visible mutations in higher plants was found by Stadler[59] and in lower plants, for moderate doses, by Hollaender and others (see review previously cited[35]).

It is true that in occasional experiments with very low doses results different from those expected on a strictly linear relation have been obtained. For instance, too few induced lethals seemed to be obtained by Caspari & Stern[4] and too many induced visibles by Bonnier & Lüning.[2] However, these experiments were carried on at dose levels so low that small sources of error had a relatively great effect. These sources of error include, in the case of visible mutations, differences in the degree of adverse selection against the mutants as between the control and the treated series, caused, for instance, by differences in the degree of crowding. In the case of both lethals and visibles, the numbers of mutations obtained at these doses are so low as to have a relatively large statistical variation. Moreover, the proportion of those obtained which were induced by the radiation is subject to a far greater error still, since it is represented by the difference between the frequency found at the low dose and that found in the control material. Inasmuch as at doses of 25 and 50 r the spontaneous (control) frequency may be a good deal higher than the induced frequency, the error of this difference may be relatively enormous. This is especially true because the spontaneous frequency itself is subject to much more variation than that of random sampling. One source of such variation lies in the origination of mutations in clusters of common origin, caused by mutations in early germ cells. Another lies in the great differences between the spontaneous mutation rates existing in different lines, which may be as great as one order of magnitude and give evidence of being caused by genes (Muller[26]), now called "mutator genes". Finally, both the spontaneous and the induced mutation rates vary considerably according to the history of the germ cells used (for example, Muller;[30] Lüning[23]). Very special techniques are necessary for minimizing these various sources of error.

In view of these difficulties it is not surprising that experiments to test the linear relation have not yet been pushed below 25 r. At Indiana University, however, over the course of several years genetic and other techniques have been worked out which should now make it possible for significant results to be obtained at doses as low as 10 or even 5 r. Work on the necessary scale would require the co-operation of a group working for some two years and examining several hundred thousand cultures—a project that we estimate might cost some $ 18 000. We are not especially desirous to carry out the study ourselves, since even if the necessary financial support were provided the work would inevitably entail much digression from our other activities. But we should be glad to co-operate by furnishing the stocks and techniques and aiding in the supervision of the work if it were to be carried out elsewhere; and if no other suitable place could be found we would not exclude the possibility of our conducting the investigation.

The fact that the relation is linear at 50 r, and even when the irradiation of the sperm cells is protracted for several weeks, makes it very probable that it remains so all the way down to zero. For, in some of this work, it can be shown that hours must have elapsed between the traversing of a sperm cell by one ionization track and its traversal by another. If, however, the linear relation can be pushed down to doses as low as 5 r (or if at this dose the frequency can merely be shown to be more nearly proportional to the dose itself than to its 1.5 or 0.5 power), then we should be able to conclude with a very high degree of assurance that the relation was indeed linear all the way down to zero. This is because the ionizations are not produced separately, but occur in the course of the tracks of the fast ionizing particles (the released electrons). Thus the ionizations come in spurts and a cell either gets a spurt or it does not. With very low doses, such as 5 r or less, an individual spermatozoon would hardly ever be traversed by more than one track, that is, it would not receive more than one spurt. Hence lowering the dose would not have the effect of lessening the number of ionizations in cells that received a spurt, but only of lessening the number of cells that received any spurt at all. For these very low doses, then, the mutation frequency would be proportional only to the number of cells "hit", which is necessarily proportional to the dose. Therefore we could justifiably extrapolate the results from 5 r linearly all the way down to zero. We need only make the one proviso here that the mutations produced in a cell by ionizing radiation result from ionizations or activations arising in that cell itself and not from those in the medium; and there is evidence from other work (see Muller[35]) that this is true of mutations produced by ionizing radiation in *Drosophila*.

Influence of Local Concentration of Activations

Even if we assumed the linear relation to hold all the way down to zero for X-rays and gamma-rays, this still would not mean that a given mutation necessarily results from just one ionization or excitation. For many of the ionizations and excitations are grouped together in small clusters in the course of the tracks of the fast particles, and it is possible that a cluster rather than a single quantum change is usually required to cause a gene mutation or chromosome break. At first sight it might be thought that this view is contradicted by the lack of influence of intensity changes on the dose—mutation rate relation, inasmuch as this result indicates that a given number of nearby ionizations when crowded together in time are no more mutagenic than when scattered in their time distribution. However, this inference is inapplicable to the question at issue, because the crowding attained in this way is much less than that within the minute clusters formed in the course of the track of a fast particle. That a cluster of such density is in fact more effective mutagenically than the same number of scattered activations is indicated by recent work (for example, Ives et al.;[14] Mickey;[24] Muller[33]) which seems to show neutrons to be more effective than X-rays in producing both point mutations and chromosome breaks. Other evidence to the same effect lies in the lower mutagenic effectiveness apparently shown by betatron radiation with an energy of about 15 Mev., as compared with ordinary X-rays, inasmuch as the radiation of higher energy is thought to result in a somewhat lesser amount of clustering than do ordinary X-rays (Herskowitz, Muller & Laughlin[12]). One may interpret the seemingly greater effectiveness of more densely crowded activations in terms of the Watson-Crick model of chromosome structure, by supposing that a hit on both complementary strands at nearly corresponding points is more likely to result in a permanent alteration in the chromosome than a hit on just one of the strands. However, the dosimetric criteria used in the works cited are still open to doubt (see Zimmer [68]).

Complications at High Doses

The breakage of chromosomes by radiation complicates in more than one way, at high doses, the relation between the radiation dose and the observed frequency of visible or lethal mutations. For one thing, the ensuing chromosome abnormalities often kill the affected cells or their descendant-cells by causing chromosome bridges at a subsequent mitosis, and, short of such an effect, can lower the multiplication rate of the descendant-cells or even kill them by means of the resulting aneuploidy (the abnormal proportions existing between different chromosome-parts). This circumstance would not in itself affect the observed frequency of point mutations were it not for the fact that germ cells in different stages of the reproductive and mitotic cycles differ from one another in their susceptibility to having their chromosomes broken, and differ in a parallel manner in their susceptibility to having point mutations induced within them. At higher doses there is necessarily more killing off of the more susceptible cells, relatively to the less susceptible ones, by means of chromosome changes, than at lower doses (as well as a greater reduction in the multiplication rate of those not actually killed). Now, since the cells of the groups more injured in this way are also the ones that have had more point mutations produced in them, it follows that at high doses there is more selective elimination (or reduction in relative numbers) of the germ cells containing point mutations as compared with the unmutated ones than there is at low doses. Hence, at higher and higher doses the frequency of point mutations observed among the offspring will fall further and further short (in a relative sense) of the frequency with which the point mutations had actually been produced, and the graph of the observed results will bend down ever further from the straight line extrapolated from the data obtained at low and moderate doses.

It is evident that the more heterogeneous the susceptibilities of the group of irradiated germ cells from which the given offspring are derived, the more pronounced will the falling off from linearity be. A very marked illustration of this effect, involving only a one-and-a-half-fold increase in observed lethal mutation frequency with a four-fold increase in dose (from 1000 to 4000 r), was obtained (Muller et al. [40]) by taking offspring from copulations of *Drosophila* males that had occurred 7 to 10 days after their irradiation as newly hatched imagos. The reason the effect was here so marked was because, as Lüning's work already referred to had shown, the germ cells released during this period were at the time of irradiation in a number of different stages, having widely different susceptibilities. Although the irradiation of a completely homogeneous group of germ cells would, theoretically, fail to give rise to any such effect, this has so far, in *Drosophila*, remained an ideal situation that has probably not been obtained in practice.

Even gonial cells are of differing mutagenic susceptibilities, depending, for one thing, upon whether or not they happen to be in mitosis at the time of irradiation. As Oster[45] has shown, gonial cells containing the condensed chromosomes of mitotic stages (produced in this case by colchicine or acenaphthene treatment) are, like other cells with condensed chromosomes, more susceptible to radiation mutagenesis. This fits in with Russell's finding that the mutation frequencies observed on examination of mice derived from irradiated spermatogonia, although linear for the dose range 300 r to 600 r, fell markedly below the expectation for linearity when a dose of 1000 r was used.

In organisms such as *Drosophila* and, probably, moulds, in which mutations of visible or lethal expression can arise in connexion with gross structural changes of chromosomes, either as position effects or as deficiencies, the complication exists that the frequency of these structural changes rises more rapidly than the dose (approximately as its 3/2 power[28,29]). The observed mutants, unless analysed for gross structural changes, will represent a mixture of these and point mutations (the latter in turn consisting of gene mutations and minute structural changes, both of which vary linearly with the dose). Thus at lower doses, where the great majority of the mutations are in the point category, the frequency will be linearly related to the dose, but at high doses, where the gross structural changes become numerically important, it might be expected that the over-all frequency of lethal and of visible mutations would gradually rise, to approach the 3/2 power relation. Such a rise in frequency is seen in the results for visible mutations observed by Stapleton, Hollaender & Martin[60]) after irradiation of spores of the mould *Aspergillus*; but the offspring obtained after irradiation of mature *Drosophila* males have in most experiments seemed to show a linear relation for lethal and for visible mutations even at high doses. The explanation of this result, which at first sight seems paradoxical, is doubtless to be sought in the fact that in the experiments with *Drosophila* the germ cells used were heterogeneous enough when irradiated to result in a tendency of the frequency to fall off from linearity, in consequence of selective elimination of the products of the more susceptible germ cells, and that this tendency largely compensated for the rise above linearity that would otherwise have been produced by the ever greater relative numbers of structural-change mutants arising at the higher doses.

Because of these complications results with high doses are apt to be erratic and difficult of analysis. Thus observations with moderate doses are better suited for arriving at an understanding of the fundamental frequency-dose relationship. [a]

Influence of Cell Type on Induced Mutation Rate

It has long been known (see, for example, Stadler;[59] Muller[27]) that cells of different types or stages differ considerably in their susceptibility to mutagenesis by ionizing radiation. Although gross structural changes of chromosomes show the most variation in frequency with cell type, point mutations (including what are probably changes within a gene as well as minute deficiencies and rearrangements of one to a few genes) probably have a frequency range of at least four-fold when a given dose is applied to different types of germ cells. This is to be concluded both from results on lethals arising at moderate doses (at which relatively few of the changes are in gross chromosome structure) and from visible mutations found by cytological observation to be free of discernible changes in the chromosomes.

Putting together the results of earlier and later studies (see review previously cited [35] and also recent papers by Bonnier & Lüning,[3] Telfer & Abrahamson,[62] Abrahamson & Telfer,[1] and Oster[47]), we find that the early germ cells and gonia have the lowest frequency of induced point mutations yet the highest ratio of point mutations to changes of any kind that can be demonstrated to be structural (i.e., in these cells the structural changes fall to a minimum which is relatively much lower still). At these stages, the mutation frequency and distribution of types is much the same in male and female. In the later male germ cells, the over-all mutation frequency, including that of recessive lethals, rises to a sharp maximum during the period of spermatid formation and transformation (although we must omit the preceding meiotic stages from consideration here as not being well enough known in this respect). Lüning has given reasons for inferring that much or all of the exceptionally high frequency of recessive lethals induced in the spermatid period involves those connected with gross and minute structural changes of chromosomes rather than true gene mutations. The over-all mutation frequency, including that of recessive lethals, then falls sharply from the spermatid period to a second minimum in the immature spermatozoa (a minimum not nearly as low, however, as the preceding one in the gonia), only to rise again within the next few days until the time of ejaculation. After insemination, within the reproductive tract of the female, the male germ cells attain, and maintain at a relatively constant level, their highest known frequency of recessive lethals as well as of demonstrable structural changes, except for that found in the spermatids.

---

a) Since the foregoing was written, C.W. Edington has reported finding, in *Drosophila*, the expected rise above linearity at higher doses (see *Genetics*, 1956, 41, 814). — H.J.M., 30 April 1957.

In rodents, the fact has long been known that ionizing radiation has a far more damaging effect on the genetic material when applied to mature or nearly mature male germ cells than when applied to immature ones (gonia), as judged by the killing of the resulting embryos. It remained for Snell[58] to provide evidence that these effects, and the inherited "semi-sterility" which he found also to be induced in mice, were caused by gross structural changes of chromosomes, a class of effects with which we are not primarily concerned in this paper. Later, however, evidence was obtained by Hertwig[13] that at these same stages there is also a relatively high frequency of production of point mutations by ionizing radiation, just as was known to be true in *Drosophila*. Fortunately, in man, the period during which the germ cells of the male remain in the gonial stage is over a hundred times longer than that of the spermatid and spermatozoon stages, so that the high susceptibility of the latter stages presents a relatively minor practical problem. Thus it is the less mutable gonia of mammals, studied mainly by Russell, which are of greater interest in assessing the genetic damage produced by radiation in human populations. As noted earlier (see page 31), however, gonia themselves do not constitute one homogeneous class so far as susceptibility to mutagenesis is concerned, but may differ considerably, according to their developmental and mitotic stage, and perhaps also their physiological condition.

As for the female germ cells, the point mutation frequency in the late oocytes of *Drosophila*, during the last three or four days before ovulation, attains a level almost as high as that in the nearly mature unejaculated spermatozoa, when high doses of radiation are used (Muller, Valencia & Valencia[43]). However, in the previously mentioned work of Herskowitz & Abrahamson it was found that lethals induced at this stage show dependence on a higher power of the dose than 1, and on the timing of the dose, as well as other peculiarities, all indicating that a high proportion of them consists of small structural changes involving two independently produced chromosome breaks. These mutations (like many of those induced in spermatids and spermatozoa), although not strictly point mutations, must usually be classed with them operationally, since the making of the distinction is commonly impracticable or even impossible.

In mammals the germ cells of females may, according to one view, remain for a long time in a stage corresponding to the late oocytes of *Drosophila*. It will therefore be important to determine to what extent mammalian female germ cells follow similar principles to those of *Drosophila* late oocytes in regard to induced mutations. If they remain long in such a stage, we should have to admit a notable departure from linearity for female germ cells. Whatever the answer may be, however, it is to be expected that for low doses, such as those received in most occupational and diagnostic exposures, the frequency would be linearly proportional to dose even in late oocytes (because any given mutagenically sensitive region is so seldom traversed by more than one track), and that the frequency for a given low dose would not be lower in them than in gonia.

That somatic cells, like germ cells, can have point mutations induced in them by ionizing radiation was first shown by Patterson,[48] using *Drosophila* embryos and larvae. Calculations which the writer made on the basis of Patterson's early results, confirmed by studies by Timoféeff-Ressovsky [63] and, more recently, by Lefevre,[20] show that for given genes the frequency of point mutations is similar to that obtained for gonia, though perhaps somewhat higher. This point is of importance in considerations of those effects of radiation on the exposed individual himself, such as leukaemia and other malignancies, which might have their basis in point mutations of his somatic cells.[a]

With the development by Puck and his co-workers of methods for culturing and subculturing human somatic cells like micro-organisms, for finding and breeding lines of mutant cells,[51] and for determining the effects of different doses of ionizing radiation,[50] the way has now been paved for carrying forward to man the exact study of the induction of point mutations and other genetic changes in somatic cells. From this study, some evidence has already been adduced (Puck & Marcus [50]) that the killing effect of the radiation on the cells is, as was to have been expected, caused by chromosome structural change rather than point mutation. It is probable on a number of grounds that this genetic killing of individual cells and genetic impairment of others, caused by gross chromosome changes, lies at the root of much of the damaging effect of radiation on the body of the exposed individual, such as epilation, leucocytopenia, destruction of the intestinal lining and other manifestations of radiation sickness, production of cataracts, retardation and distortion of growth, reduction of regenerative capacity, and—probably the most important effect—reduction of the life-span (see discussions by Muller,[32,38] Quastler,[52] and Sacher [55]).

Estimation of Total Damage from Point Mutations

The prime questions regarding the damage done to posterity by a given amount of radiation are: what will the total amount of that damage be, and how will it be distributed? In the previous sections we have discussed how the frequency of lethal or visible mutations varies with dose and with types of cell, but we have not considered the absolute frequency of such mutations for any given dose, still less the total frequency of mutations of all kinds. It is this total frequency that counts. For, as shown long ago by Haldane [9] and developed later by Muller,[31] in a population at mutational equilibrium

---

a) For a recent treatment of radiation-induced leukaemia from this viewpoint, involving a calculation of its frequency per roentgen, see Lewis, E. B. (1957) *Science*, **125** (in press). — H. J. M., 30 April 1957.

(i.e., a population in which about as many mutant genes are dying out in each generation through death, or failure to reproduce, of the individuals containing them as are arising anew through mutation) the average reduction in fitness of an individual lies between the total frequency of all detrimental mutations, counting equally those with large and those with small effects, and twice that frequency. If all the mutant genes were strictly recessive, the lower figure (the mutation rate, μ, itself) would apply, whereas if they were all dominant enough to be eliminated as heterozygotes the figure would be twice this (2μ). As Muller [31] pointed out, there is good reason for assuming the higher figure, 2μ, to be nearly correct both in *Drosophila* and in man. This same figure for reduction of fitness would on the whole express the proportion of individuals in the population who would have to suffer "genetic death" (selective elimination by death before maturity or failure to reproduce) to maintain the genetic equilibrium. Some reduction of the figure for the elimination rate (probably by not more than a factor of 2) might, however, have to be made to allow for some synergistic operation by detrimental genes: a mode of action giving individuals with multiple defects a lower survival rate than the product of the survival rates of those with the separate defects.

In estimating this total mutation rate for practical purposes only point mutations need usually be considered, since the great majority both of spontaneous mutations and of those that would be likely to be produced by radiation in a human population are of this nature. The first approach towards determining the total mutation rate in any organism was made independently and simultaneously in 1934-35 by Kerkis (working in collaboration with the writer) and by Timoféeff-Ressovsky, using descendants of irradiated *Drosophila* males. [16,65] Special techniques were used for the detection of mutations which have neither a visible nor a fully lethal effect, but only reduce the expectation of survival to maturity: the so-called "detrimental" mutations. Both studies showed that these detrimental mutations arose some three to four times as frequently as the fully lethal mutations. Essentially similar results have recently been reported by Käfer,[15] working under the guidance of Hadorn, and Falk,[7] working under the guidance of Bonnier.

It is admitted by all these investigators, however, that with their techniques there was little chance of detecting mutations that reduced survival up to maturity by less than some 5-10%. Moreover, there must be many mutations, undetectable by these techniques, the detrimental effect of which occurs mainly after maturity is reached or which affect reproductive capacity rather than individual survival. Thus the estimate that in *Drosophila* there are some 5 times as many harmful mutations altogether as the number of lethals, and some 30 times the number of sex-linked lethals, is a bare minimum, possibly only half the true value. It now becomes of great importance to extend the range of detected mutations to those with still less effect, and with other types of effect, so as to throw light on the extent to which the present estimate should be raised. As in the case of the proposed investigation of low dosage, we have for some years been developing techniques for carrying out such a study in *Drosophila*, but again the work would necessarily be on so large a scale that team-work and considerable expenditure (comparable in magnitude with that for the low-dosage project) would be required.

In absolute numbers the above estimate becomes for a dose of, say, 100 r applied to the spermatozoa of young *Drosophila* males a day or two before their mating, and applied to late oocytes, about one induced mutation in every 12 germ cells or one in every 6 offspring. Thus a continuation of this exposure, applied to both sexes through many successive generations, would reduce the average fitness of the individual in the equilibrium population by about a sixth (some 17%) and would cause about one individual in 6 to meet "genetic death" in consequence of the irradiation. It can further be estimated (see below) that the total effect of spontaneous mutations in *Drosophila* is about half as great as this; that is, the given amount of radiation, applied at the stages specified, would constitute about twice the "doubling dose". But it should be borne in mind that these present estimates are in both cases minimal ones.

Manner of Distribution and Expression of the Total Damage

How does this mutational damage become distributed and expressed among the descendants? The amount of damage done by any given mutant gene in a heterozygous descendant may be represented as the amount of detrimental effect it would exert when homozygous multiplied by its amount of dominance (the ratio of its effect when heterozygous to that when homozygous). Now the dominance of lethals in *Drosophila* has been found both by Stern and his co-workers (see Stern et al.[61]) and by the present author and Campbell (see Morton, Crow & Muller[25]) to average about 0.04 to 0.05, so that even these mutant genes with extreme effects would individually reduce viability in the heterozygote by only some 5%. The merely detrimental genes are suspected on theoretical grounds (Muller[31]) to have somewhat more dominance than the lethals, and there has recently been some direct evidence for this (Falk[7]); but, even when considerable allowance is made for this possibility, the effect exerted in a heterozygote by a detrimental is expected, on the average, to be less, absolutely, than that exerted by a lethal. Thus, taking individual mutant genes of all degrees, they should average well below 5% in individually lowering the fitness of the heterozygote. Since at the same time the visible effects of these genes in the heterozygote, *taken individually*, usually escape notice, it follows that the effects of mutations induced by radiation in any one generation at a frequency comparable with that considered above would not ordinarily be observed among the next or any subsequent generation. Nevertheless, the total loss of fitness in the next generation, being about one in 6 (the minimum frequency of offspring with newly induced mutations) times, say, 1 % (to take a bare minimum for their average expression in heterozygotes) would in a population of 1 000 000 entail the "genetic death" of at least 1700 individuals of that generation. Moreover, a comparable amount of damage would continue to be exerted for scores of generations.

The number of generations through which a mutant gene persists before causing genetic death is on the average approximately the reciprocal of the amount of damage it does to the heterozygote, so that the average *Drosophila* lethal in an autosome might be expected to persist for some 22 generations. However, the average persistence of a group of mutant genes is the *harmonic*, not the arithmetic, mean of the persistence of the individual mutant genes, and this value for the *Drosophila* lethals investigated turns out to be about 50 generations, though with a high error (see Morton, Crow & Muller [25]). The persistence of detrimentals must be even greater. This is the so-called "accumulation figure", which represents not only the average persistence of the mutant genes arising in a given generation, but also the average amount of overlapping, within the individuals of any given generation, of the mutant genes that arose in different generations, provided that the same mutation rate has existed in successive generations for a long period and mutational equilibrium has therefore been established. Hence if the 100 r exposure postulated above were to be applied to *Drosophila* for many generations it is to be expected that each generation would be damaged by an amount at least 50 times greater than that calculated above for the first generation of offspring (in fact, by an amount equal to 2μ or, in this case, 17%). Moreover, instead of one individual in six carrying a mutant gene induced by the radiation, each individual would contain at least $50 \times 1/6$, or at least eight of them, on the average. Thus, although the effects of the mutant genes would seldom be individually noticed, their collective effect would in the great majority of individuals be quite appreciable. It would of course tend to give a different pattern of impairment from one individual to another.

The Induced in Relation to the Spontaneous Mutational Damage

The damage caused by the induced mutations is of course intermingled with that caused by spontaneous mutations. Although the amount of the radiation-induced mutational damage is largely independent of that caused by the spontaneous mutations, it is helpful, in grasping its meaning, to compare it with that of the naturally existing mutational impairment, since a species is in a sense adjusted to the latter and since, in man, we have a rough pragmatic familiarity with it. For this purpose it is desirable to be able to express spontaneous mutations in the same terms as those used above for induced mutations—namely, in terms of total mutation rate and loss of fitness. This is easily done, once estimates of these total values have been made for the *induced* mutations occurring at some given dose, provided only that the frequency of some particular group of mutations, e.g., sex-linked lethals, or visibles of a given collection or category (but preferably not those confined to just one allele-series), has been determined under comparable circumstances both in unirradiated and in irradiated material. For there is good reason to believe that,│for point mutations, the following relation will approximately hold: total spontaneous mutations/spontaneous mutations of a given category = total induced mutations/induced mutations of the same category. Thus, if figures are obtainable for the last three terms, an estimate for the first one (the spontaneous total) can be calculated. The particular category best determined and most used for this purpose in *Drosophila* work has been that of sex-linked lethals.

Any *one* particular allele-series (or "locus") cannot be relied upon by itself for the above purpose because the frequencies of mutation of different series may not bear the same relation to one another for spontaneous as for radiation-induced or otherwise induced mutations (see, for example, Giles [8]). However, there is no reason to suspect that any broad phenotypic category or section of chromatin, or a whole group of allele-series chosen for their technical convenience, will show any consistent preference as between spontaneous and radiation-induced mutability. Experimental evidence that there is no such differential susceptibility in *Drosophila* was obtained in the observation, by Timoféeff-Ressovsky,[66] the writer (see Patterson & Muller [49]), and others, of the similar ratio of sex-linked lethals to sex-linked visibles in both unirradiated and irradiated material (especially when allowance is made for the relatively higher frequency of deficiencies and other structural changes after irradiation).

As noted earlier, the ratio of "total" mutations to sex-linked lethals in *Drosophila* when radiation is used has been estimated to be at least 30, and we may therefore, in accordance with the above formula, multiply the spontaneous sex-linked lethal frequency by 30 to obtain the spontaneous total. The problem arises, however, of what observed value of the spontaneous sex-linked lethal frequency to choose. For this value has been found to vary by at least one order of magnitude from one experiment to another according to the stocks used (Muller,[26] confirmed by later workers), and by more than half an order of magnitude according to the developmental history of the germ cells (Muller,[30] and unpublished data), not to speak of the variations caused by temperature and other environmental differences within the natural range. However, the upshot of a large number of studies of the spontaneous sex-linked lethal frequency in *Drosophila*, by different investigators, has shown that the great majority of individuals bred at 25°C under reasonably favourable conditions, in such a manner that the germ cells used to produce the offspring do not give undue representation to those with extreme developmental histories, have a sex-linked lethal frequency averaging about 0.1% to 0.2%. This is true in both sexes, but the female value appears to vary less with germ-cell history and commonly to approximate 0.17%, whereas the male value, which is higher (0.2%) for the sperm released very early, is a good deal lower (e.g., 0.06%) for those released in what might be called the prime of life. Taking 0.14% as a reasonable average and multiplying it by 30, our minimum figure for the total spontaneous mutation rate per gamete is 4.2% and that for the zygote is 8.4%, a figure which also represents the average reduction in fitness or risk of genetic death as a result of spontaneous mutations. It was on the basis of this estimate that an irradiation of 100 r given to *Drosophila* in the manner specified earlier (see page 36) was there stated to constitute about twice the doubling dose, inasmuch as it had been calculated to give an induced rate of 17% per zygote.

From the above it will be seen that, in *Drosophila* at least, there is much more uncertainty about the amount of spontaneous mutational damage, because of the high variability of the spontaneous mutation rate, than about the damage caused by any given amount of radiation applied to a known stage or group of stages. Because of this uncertainty, determinations of the spontaneous mutation rate of any particular category of mutants in *Drosophila*, such as a given group of "visibles", should always, in order to have significance in relation to other work, be accompanied by a yardstick indicating the general mutability characteristic of the material studied. At present the most convenient such yardstick is to be found in the sex-linked lethal rate, which must be ascertained under precisely the same conditions. Only when such a yardstick is provided can we, for example, use data on the frequency of spontaneous mutations of given types to estimate the ratio they bear to the total mutation frequency, or to the frequency of some other particular category, inasmuch as these other quantities themselves are properly expressed in relation to a corresponding yardstick.

It is true that the radiation-induced rate also varies to some extent according to the stocks used (see below), the environmental conditions, and the germ-cell stages involved. These differences, however, are not usually likely to throw out our reckoning nearly so much as in the case of spontaneous mutations, since we have more knowledge of how they may be allowed for. But they must be taken into account.

Species Differences and the Problem of Extrapolation

In view of the evidence already referred to of the variation in the radiation-induced frequency of point mutations in *Drosophila* according to the type of cell irradiated, and the abundant evidence that has been obtained in recent years of the influence of conditions associated with the irradiation, such as oxygen concentration, enzyme-inhibitors, etc., on the frequency (see author's review [35]), it would be strange if genetic differences failed to affect the result.   Indeed, Dubovsky [6] reported that some stocks of *D. melanogaster* from widely separated localities differed by a factor of about two in the frequency of lethals produced by irradiation of the male. It is true that such differences can be produced in the same stock by slight differences in the timing of the germ cells used, a fact not then realized, and that stocks may also differ genetically in their natural timing, but genetic differences of many kinds would be expected to be capable of influencing the result.   In the light of these considerations, however, it is rather noteworthy that, contrariwise, even the specific difference between *D. simulans* and *D. melanogaster* was found by Kossikov [18] not to be associated with a significant difference between the induced frequencies of lethals in flies of these two kinds.   This similarity may indicate that the induced frequency, like the spontaneous one (see below), even though readily altered, tends to be maintained at a certain level by some active selective processes operating on features that, perhaps as a by-product, tend to maintain susceptibility to these mutagenic factors at the level found.

However that may be, it is not to be expected that widely different species, such as those of different phyla, would have similar induced or spontaneous mutation frequencies, either total or of any given over-all phenotypic class and/or chromosomal type (such as sterility mutations or sex-linked lethals), nor that they would have a similar ratio of total mutation rate to mutation rate in such a category.   One reason for this disparity is that the amount and distribution of the genetic material must differ enormously as between such organisms; another is that the processes whereby the genes reach expression must be so different that a superficial resemblance in effect would provide little or no indication of a homologous genetic basis.   Thus even if the frequency of production of, for example, sex-linked lethals were known in a mammal, one certainly would not be justified in multiplying this figure by the *Drosophila* factor of 30, to estimate the total frequency of induced mutations in the mammal.

The case is, however, different when we use as our index of relative mutation rates in two widely different species a category consisting of the average frequency of origination, in each species, of members of a single allele (or pseudo-allele) series, often called the "specific-locus rate", provided that this average has been determined through observations of a number of different series ("loci") in each species and that most of the values found for the different series of the same species show (as they have done) a tendency to be clustered within about one order of magnitude.   The reasonable agreement between the results for some 12 different allele-series involving visible point mutations (including those that are at the same time lethal) after irradiation of the spermatozoa of *Drosophila* (Muller,[34] and unpublished data) and also for some 7 series after irradiation of the spermatogonia of mice (Russell;[53, 54] Kimball [17]), justifies us in speaking of an average or modal induced mutability for such an allele-series in each species. We may then infer that differences in the detectability of the mutations of the different series, in the complexity of the genetic regions concerned, and in their actual mutability, are usually insufficient to cause inordinate discrepancies between the values for the different series.

In *Drosophila* the ratio between the "total" and the average single allele-series rate is at least 10 000 (for example, Muller [36]) and is probably a good deal higher. This value has been obtained by multiplying the ratio of "all" detrimentals and lethals to sex-linked lethals by the ratio of the latter to the average single allele-series frequency. (These two constituent ratios have of course been obtained in different experiments, under different conditions.) Are we now justified in assuming that a mammal would have at least as high a ratio as a fly of the "total" to the average single allele-series rate, and may we therefore multiply the latter rate, as determined in Russell's irradiation experiments, by 10 000, to obtain a minimum value for the total induced mutation rate in mice?

The justification for this procedure lies almost entirely in general considerations. The main consideration is that a mammal, by no matter what criterion, stands at least as high in the scale of biological organization as a fly, and probably a good deal higher as judged by its complexity of gross and histological structure, physiology, and behaviour. It would therefore be surprising if the genetic basis of the mammal were not at least as complicated and, accordingly, compounded of as many parts (such as nucleotides) as that of the fly. This would imply also that it had at least as many, and probably more, different ways of mutating, and that any one allele-series, on the average, represented no larger, but probably a smaller, fraction of all the mutational potentialities in the case of the mammal than in the case of the fly. The several times greater DNA content of the mammalian than of the *Drosophila* chromosome-set tends to support this inference.

It is to be noted that this method of obtaining a minimum estimate of the total induced rate in the mouse avoids any assumptions regarding the means of defining the limits of a gene or locus, and the number of such entities. It is true that in the past the argument has usually been stated in terms of genes or loci (but see Muller [36, 37, 39]), but this has, for the present writer at least, been only a short-cut mode of expression. For, what was meant by the "specific locus" frequency was really the frequency with which mutations arose that were on operational grounds to be classed as probably being members of the same allele-series, without assumptions being made as to what proportion of mutations actually occurring in the chromosome region in question would fall into the given allele category. Moreover, although 10 000 was sometimes stated to be a minimum value of the number of genes or loci, as estimated by several very different methods, the justification for using it also as the ratio of total mutations to mutations in one average allele-series ("specific locus") was that, empirically, the experiments on detrimental mutations, lethals, and allele-series mutations had shown this ratio to hold, irrespective of the number of genes or the way in which they were defined. It is quite possible, for instance, that some of the same chromosome regions that gave rise by mutation to members of a given visible allele-series also gave rise to lethals and/or detrimentals (which may or may not have been included in the count of the allele-series frequency, according to whether or not they also produced the visible effect that served as the criterion), but this was irrelevant to the determination of the ratio since all the lethals and detrimentals of sufficient detectability to be recorded as such were included in the measurement of the frequency of these classes and therefore in the "total" rate. Thus the only relevant questions concerning the validity of the extrapolation process for obtaining a minimum estimate are whether or not a sufficiently representative sample of allele-series has been obtained, and whether we are willing to admit the probability of the proposition that the average allele-series, as operationally defined, would contribute at least as small a fraction of the total mutation rate in a mammal as in a fly.

If we grant these points and apply our factor of 10 000 to Russell's observed allele-series rate of 25×10^{-8} mutations per r in the spermatogonia of mice, we find as our minimum estimate of the total induced frequency in this material 25×10^{-4}, which may also be expressed by saying that there is at least one mutation per germ cell for every 400 r. As for the human induced mutation rate, we can at present only say that this is what it would be if it were like that of mice, that there are no data from man as yet that are inconsistent with this, and that this rate is about one order of magnitude higher than the induced rate in *Drosophila*.

On the other hand, we do have for man, as well as for the mouse, some data that allow us to estimate the spontaneous mutation frequency for allele-series. As this matter has recently been discussed elsewhere (Muller [39]), the writer will not attempt an appraisal of the validity of this evidence here, beyond pointing out, first, that the determination for man has the advantage of being based on large-scale data that give, as it were, a cross-section of results from different genetic lines and from different ages and conditions of reproduction, and, secondly, that the results of the different allele-series agree reasonably well with each other and, what is more surprising, that their consensus agrees well with the average based on mice.

Here again, then, is evidence of the operation of selective processes that tend to stabilize the mutation rate, as was noted earlier (see page 40) in connexion with the radiation-induced rate. Even more striking evidence of this, in the case of spontaneous mutation, is the unexpected similarity between both these human and mouse values for the spontaneous allele-series rate and that (in the neighbourhood of 0.5×10^{-5}) deduced to be characteristic of *Drosophila*. It is true that thus far there has only been one published experiment (Muller, Valencia & Valencia [42]) in which a considerable group of spontaneous allele-series rates in *Drosophila* has been directly determined and in which, at the same time, a yardstick (sex-linked lethals) was used so that the rates obtained could be converted (as proved necessary) into more typical ones. However, approximately the same figure had been reached earlier by taking the typical spontaneous sex-linked lethal rate and dividing it by the ratio found to hold between the induced sex-linked lethal rate and the induced allele-series rate. Moreover, confirmation of the order of magnitude of this value (although probably involving some reduction of the value itself) is now being obtained in another series of direct observations, checked by lethals, conducted by Schalet in our laboratory at Indiana University. In any case, such a correspondence between such different species tends to impart confidence in the estimated orders of magnitude.

When, now, the factor of 10 000 is applied to the estimated value for an allele-series in man, taking for the latter the rather conservative figure of 10^{-5}, we find that the minimum estimate of the "total" spontaneous mutation rate turns out to be 0.1 per gamete or 0.2 per individual, a value higher than has commonly been suspected to apply to our own species.

Light from Another Source

Extrapolation of the type discussed above is not the only means of arriving at estimates of the spontaneous mutation rate in man on the basis of existing data. As explained by Morton, Crow & Muller [25] in a parallel paper (see also Crow [5] and Muller [39]), several different studies of the mortality found among the offspring of consanguineous as compared with non-consanguineous matings in man agree reasonably well in giving evidence from which it can be deduced that the average human gamete carries a mutational load accumulated from past generations which, if it became homozygous, would be twice as great as needed to kill the individual bearing it at some time between a late foetal and an early adult stage. Much of this load is probably scattered among diverse mutant genes any one of which would, if homozygous, entail a relatively small risk of death. There must in addition be a considerable load of detrimental genes in the gamete that tend to cause death before or after the period studied, or that interfere with reproduction rather than with survival. Moreover, in a population living under more primitive conditions than those studied, more genes would find such expression than did so in the given populations. Finally, the individual himself carries twice as many such genes as the gamete. All in all, then, the load carried, mainly heterozygously, by the gamete is probably (if expressed in terms of the damage it would do homozygously) as much as about 8 "lethal equivalents".

Now this rather directly measured load does not in itself tell us anything of the mutation rate per generation. However, if there are means of obtaining a reasonable estimate, by extrapolation or otherwise, of the relative amount of expression which this load actually attains in the average individual (a matter dependent upon the degree of dominance of the mutant genes and on the frequency with which occasional homozygosity occurs), we should then have a value for the average reduction in fitness. As noted previously, this would be almost equal to μ (the total spontaneous mutation rate) if the eliminations in the given population are brought about mainly through the homozygous effects and almost 2μ if the dominance is enough for elimination usually to be caused by the heterozygous effects. Now although the data from man are insufficient to allow us to set a value for the average dominance of mutant genes, there are considerations (pointed out in some of the papers cited above) that allow us to set some fairly reasonable limits to such a value. Moreover, the value found for *Drosophila* lethals lies well between these limits. It is also possible to arrive at reasonable limits for the frequency of homozygosity caused by inbreeding. If then we extrapolate by taking the value for dominance found in *Drosophila*, and at the same time use in our reckoning the human inbreeding factor, we reach a value for reduction in fitness of approximately 0.1 per gamete or 0.2 per individual. This in turn gives us, as the value for the "total" spontaneous mutation rate, $\mu = 0.1$ per gamete, as was estimated by the other method, explained in the foregoing section.

It must be pointed out that the present method involves data and methods of calculation both of which are entirely separate, as well as different in character, from those used in the other mode of attack. Although extrapolation is employed at one point in the present attack—namely, for estimating the degree of dominance—this item did not enter at all into the earlier calculation. Moreover, there seems little doubt, in the light of observations concerned with man himself (see, for example, Levit [21]), that the dominance factor in man would at least be within the same order of magnitude as that assumed here on the basis of extrapolation. If this is true, then the estimate for mutation rate arrived at here is likewise of the right order of magnitude, at least as a minimum value. A further circumstance to be taken into consideration in evaluation of the present result is that it was not realized until the calculations were carried through that they would give a value even distantly in agreement with what had been obtained by the other method, and that no attempt was made to manipulate them to obtain a satisfactory fit to expectation. For these reasons, it would seem that the present result, although itself involving extrapolation, lends material support, from an independent direction, to that arrived at previously.

Although the present mode of attack is concerned only with spontaneous mutations, the estimate of the total spontaneous rate, as well as of the total load, thereby arrived at affords an important independent possibility for gauging the total mutational damage which would be produced in a human population by radiation. Before this could be accomplished, however, there would have to be some means of determining, for some limited genetic category capable of being used as an index, the relation between the spontaneous rate and the rate induced by a given dose of radiation. Possibly somatic or tissue-culture mutations, if there were good reason to assume them to be of the point type, would be useful for providing such an index. At any rate, if it were once furnished, it would then be relatively easy to combine this information with that on the total load, derived from the results of inbreeding, so as to obtain a realistic view of the all-round and long-term meaning of a given dose of radiation.

Of course we are far from the final or exact answers concerning the total frequency of either induced or spontaneous mutations, or concerning the persistence factor, for any lower organism; and we are much further yet from these answers for man. But the ways are opening up, and there seems good reason to believe that our present estimates for man, although involving extrapolation, may with assurance be regarded as minimal ones, and of the right order of magnitude. Before this point could be arrived at it was necessary to carry out a vast amount of work in the genetics of lower organisms, and also to collect very considerable data from man, and to consider these in connexion with one another. An increasing attack along both lines will be necessary if we are to attain the knowledge we need for the adequate protection and the fostering of our most precious trust, our genetic heritage.

REFERENCES

1. Abrahamson, S. & Telfer, J. D. (1956) *Genetics*, **41**, 677
2. Bonnier, G. & Lüning, K. G. (1949) *Hereditas, (Lund)*, **35**, 163
3. Bonnier, G. & Lüning, K. G. (1953) *Hereditas (Lund)*, **39**, 193
4. Caspari, E. & Stern, C. (1948) *Genetics*, **33**, 75
5. Crow, J. F. (1956) *Eugen. Quart.*, **3**, 201
6. Dubovsky, N. V. (1935) *C.R. Acad. Sci. U.R.S.S.* (n.s.), **4**, 95
7. Falk, R. (1955) *Hereditas (Lund)*, **41**, 259
8. Giles, N. H., jr (1952) *Cold Spr. Harb. Symp. quant. Biol.*, **16**, 283
9. Haldane, J. B. S. (1937) *Amer. Nat.*, **71**, 337
10. Hanson, F. B. & Heys, F. (1929) *Amer. Nat.*, **63**, 511
11. Herskowitz, I. H. & Abrahamson, S. (1956) *Genetics*, **41**, 646
12. Herskowitz, I. H., Muller, H. J. & Laughlin, J. S. (1956) *Genetics*, **41**, 646
13. Hertwig, P. (1941) *Erbänderungen bei Mäusen nach Röntgenbestrahlung.* In : *Proceedings of the Seventh International Congress of Genetics, Edinburgh, 1939* (*J. Genet.*, Suppl.), p. 145

14. Ives, P. T., Levine. R. P. & Yost, H. T., jr (1954) *Proc. nat. Acad. Sci. (Wash.)*, **40**, 165
15. Käfer, E. (1952) *Z. indukt. Abstamm.- u. VererbLehre*, **84**, 508
16. Kerkis, J. J. (1938) *Izv. Akad. Nauk SSSR (Otd. mat.-est., Ser. biol.)*, pp. 67, 75
17. Kimball, A. W. (1956) *Amer. Nat.*, **90**, 369
18. Kossikov, K. V. (1935) *Bull. Inst. Genet. Acad. Sci. U.R.S.S.*, **10**, 189
19. Kossikov, K. V. (1936) *C. R. Acad. Sci. U.R.S.S.* (n.s.), **2** (**11**), 115
20. Lefevre, G. (1950) *Amer. Nat.*, **84**, 341
21. Levit, S. G. (1936) *J. Genet.*, **33**, 411
22. Lewis, D. (1951) *Heredity*, **5**, 399
23. Lüning, K. (1952) *Studies on X-ray induced mutations in various stages of spermatogenesis in* Drosophila melanogaster, Stockholm (Thesis)
24. Mickey, G. H. (1954) *Amer. Nat.*, **88**, 241
25. Morton, N. E., Crow, J. F. & Muller, H. J. (1956) *Proc. nat. Acad. Sci. (Wash.)*, **42**, 855
26. Muller, H. J. (1928) *Genetics*, **13**, 279
27. Muller, H. J. (1930) *Amer. Nat.*, **64**, 220
28. Muller, H. J. (1938) *Collect. Net (Woods Hole)*, **13**, 181, 198
29. Muller, H. J. (1940) *J. Genet.*, **40**, 1
30. Muller, H. J. (1946) *Yearb. Amer. philos. Soc.*, *1945*, p. 150
31. Muller, H. J. (1950) *Amer. J. hum. Genet.*, **2**, 111
32. Muller, H. J. (1950) *Amer. Sci.*, **38**, 399
33. Muller, H. J. (1954) *Genetics*, **39**, 985
34. Muller, H. J. (1954) *The nature of the genetic effects produced by radiation*. In: Hollaender, A., ed., *Radiation biology*, New York, vol. 1, p. 351
35. Muller, H. J. (1954) *The manner of production of mutations by radiation*. In: Hollaender, A., ed., *Radiation biology*, New York, vol. 1, p. 475
36. Muller, H. J. (1955) *J. Hered.*, **46**, 199
37. Muller, H. J. (1956) *How radiation changes the genetic constitution*. In: United Nations, *Peaceful uses of atomic energy*, New York, vol. 11, p. 387
38. Muller, H. J. (1956) *J. Amer. Soc. Safety Engrs*, **1**, 42
39. Muller, H. J. (1957) *Further studies bearing on the load of mutations in man*. In: *Proceedings of the First International Congress of Human Genetics, Copenhagen, 1956 (Acta. genet. (Basel)*, **6**, 157)
40. Muller, H. J. et al. (1954) *Genetics*, **39**, 741
41. Muller, H. J. & Settles, F. (1927) *Anat. Rec.*, **31**, 347
42. Muller, H. J., Valencia, J. I. & Valencia, R. M. (1950) *Genetics*, **35**, 125
43. Muller, H. J., Valencia, R. M. & Valencia, J. I. (1950) *Genetics*, **35**, 126
44. Oliver, C. P. (1930) *Science*, **71**, 44
45. Oster, I. I. (1954) *Excerpta med. (Amst.), Sect. XIV*, **8**, 406
46. Oster, I. I. (1955) *Genetics*, **40**, 692
47. Oster, I. I. (1957) *Modification of X-ray mutagenesis in* Drosophila: *II. Relative sensitivity of spermatids and mature spermatozoa*. In: *Proceedings of the Fifth International Symposium on Radiobiology, Stockholm, 1956* (In press)
48. Patterson, J. T. (1928) *Science*, **68**, 41
49. Patterson, J. T. & Muller, H. J. (1930) *Genetics*, **15**, 495
50. Puck, T. T. & Marcus, P. I. (1956) *J. exp. Med.*, **103**, 653
51. Puck, T. T., Marcus, P. I. & Cieciura, S. J. (1956) *J. exp. Med.*, **103**, 273
52. Quastler, H. (1956) *Modes of acute radiation death*. In: United Nations, *Peaceful uses of atomic energy*, New York, vol. 11, p. 121
53. Russell, W. L. (1952) *Cold Spr. Harb. Symp. quant. Biol.*, **16**, 327
54. Russell, W. L. (1956) *Genetic effects of radiation in mice and their bearing on the estimation of human hazards*. In: United Nations, *Peaceful uses of atomic energy*, New York, vol. 11, p. 382

55. Sacher, G. A. (1956) *Radiology*, **67**, 250
56. Serebrovskaya, R. I. & Shapiro, N. I. (1935) *C.R. Acad. Sci. U.R.S.S.* (n.s.), **2 (11)**, 421
57. Shapiro, N. I. (1936) *C.R. Acad. Sci. U.R.S.S.* (n.s.), **2 (11)**, 119
58. Snell, G. D. (1935) *Genetics*, **20**, 545
59. Stadler, L. J. (1928) *Anat. Rec.*, **41**, 97
60. Stapleton, G. E., Hollaender, A. & Martin, F. L. (1952) *J. cell. comp. Physiol.*, **39**, Suppl. 1, p. 87
61. Stern, C. et al. (1952) *Genetics*, **37**, 413
62. Telfer, J. D. & Abrahamson, S. (1954) *Drosophila Inform. Serv.*, **28**, 161
63. Timoféeff-Ressovsky, N. W. (1929) *Amer. Nat.*, **63**, 118
64. Timoféeff-Ressosvky, N. W. (1934) *Strahlentherapie*, **49**, 463
65. Timoféeff-Ressovsky, N. W. (1934) *Strahlentherapie*, **51**, 658
66. Timoféeff-Ressovsky, N. W. (1937) *Experimentelle Mutationsforschung in der Vererbungslehre. Beeinflussung der Erbanlagen durch Strahlung und andere Faktoren*, Dresden & Leipzig (*Wiss. ForschBer.*, **42**)
67. Uphoff, D. E. & Stern, C. (1949) *Science*, **109**, 609
68 Zimmer, K. G. (1956) *Acta radiol. (Stockh.)*, **46**, 595

TYPES OF MUTATION PRODUCED AT KNOWN GENE LOCI AND POSSIBILITY OF HITHERTO UNRECOGNIZED MUTATIONS BEING INDUCED

Irradiation of Animal Populations: Results and Work Needed

T. C. CARTER

Geneticist, MRC Radiobiological Research Unit, Atomic Energy Research Establishment, Harwell, Berks, England

It is commonly accepted as a working hypothesis that ionizing radiations do not induce new types of mutation, but only raise the mutation rates of existing alleles. The basis of this assumption is partly theoretical and partly experimental. The theoretical argument rests on the fact that all living matter is continuously exposed to natural background radiation, and always has been so exposed; therefore, it is argued, any mutation which could be induced by ionizing radiation must already have been induced by natural background radiation at some time in the past; therefore no new type of mutation could be induced by man-made radiation. The experimental data, which are now extensive, do not disprove this; but in so far as the hypothesis is essentially negative, and fails to specify the extent of either spontaneous or induced mutation, it is by its very nature not amenable to experimental test. Thus, if in some experiment radiation exposure induces mutations of a type previously unknown, this can always be explained as nothing more than a manifestation of the limited nature of prior knowledge of spontaneous mutation; conversely, if exposure fails to induce mutations of a type previously known, that can always be explained as a manifestation of the finite nature of the experimental set-up. The hypothesis that ionizing radiations do not induce new types of mutation is therefore, like so many others in biology, unprovable and undisprovable. As such, it can only be of heuristic value; the extent of its value depends on our assessment of the extent to which it may be true, and the extent to which we are willing to use it as a guide in planning future action.

In point of fact, geneticists are willing to place so much faith in its validity that this hypothesis forms the basis of all present-day estimates of the genetic hazard of ionizing radiation to man. It is therefore worth while to ask if circumstances can be visualized in which it might break down. The supposition underlying it is that man-made radiations do not differ in any essential respect from natural background radiations. In respect of dose-rate they extend far beyond the natural range, but we have no clear evidence of dose-rate thresholds for the induction of genetic effects. So far as present knowledge goes, it seems that linear energy transfer is the biologically most important characteristic of a radiation; and in this respect natural background radiation covers the whole known range, from the sparse ionization of naturally occurring gamma-rays to the dense ionization produced by alpha particles and heavy cosmic nuclei. Thus there does not at present appear to be any obvious theoretical reason for expecting man-made radiations to induce alleles that were previously unknown. On the other hand, there is no theoretical basis for the converse supposition, namely, that ionizing radiation can induce all known alleles; in fact, there is a certain amount of experimental evidence that such radiation tends to induce especially the more extreme alleles at a locus.

It is worth noting that though this hypothesis has a theoretical basis which is probably valid for mutagenesis by ionizing radiations, the analogous hypothesis for chemical mutagenesis has none. There is no ground for postulating the natural occurrence in biological material of all chemical mutagens which might be synthesized in the laboratory. Furthermore, some chemical mutagens might be expected to have a relatively mild action, and induce subtle genetic changes, compared with the generally destructive action of ionizing radiation. Recent experimental work in this field—notably that of Fahmy & Fahmy [5]—supports an interpretation of this type. Furthermore, if (as seems probable) ionizing radiation is responsible for only about one-tenth of human spontaneous mutations, leaving nine-tenths to be accounted for, we should be unwise to ignore the possibility that chemical substances may be much more important than ionizing radiation as a cause of human mutation.

Thus far in this paper the gene has been considered only as the unit of mutation, its constancy between mutational events being implicit. But a gene is also a unit of action, its presence being recognizable only by its effect on the phenotype of an individual. Furthermore, the final effect of a gene, unlike the gene itself, may be extremely variable, depending upon the other allele at the same locus, the alleles at other loci and the mass of non-genetic factors, grouped together under the term "environment". In no two individuals are the total genotype and the total environment identical, and therefore in no two individuals can the same allele be expected *a priori* to produce identical end effects. Variability of gene expression may be very great where the end effect is putatively remote from the primary gene product, as with many morphological mutants; conversely, it may be relatively slight where the effect observed is believed to be close to the primary gene product, as with the blood-group antigens. In so far as the practices of civilization have wrought great changes in the macro-and micro-environment of man, we must suppose that they have changed and are changing the expression of many human alleles.

Many systems can be invented for the classification of human genes, and which particular system is used will depend on the interests of the user. The population geneticist is interested primarily in the biological value of a genotype. He will therefore classify alleles according to their average effect on the fitness of their carriers, that is to say, on the number of zygotes that will be contributed to the next generation by a zygote of the present generation. It will be a twofold classification, according as the allele is in the homozygous or heterozygous state. Mutant alleles are probably almost always disadvantageous to some extent when homozygous, but their action in heterozygotes may vary from severe detriment through neutrality to advantage. This fact divides them into two broad classes: those which are unconditionally disadvantageous, and those which are disadvantageous in some individuals but advantageous in others. The distinction is fundamental, for it determines the nature of the forces which will maintain the allele in the population and the frequency at which it will be maintained. An unconditionally detrimental allele will be maintained at a low frequency under the opposed action of mutation to the allele and natural selection against it. On the other hand, an allele which is advantageous in some individuals and disadvantageous in others will be maintained at a high frequency, depending on the degree of advantage or disadvantage in the various individuals. Mutation will play only a minor role, or even none at all, in determining the structure of the population in respect of alleles of this type. It is therefore of importance to any assessment of the genetical hazards of radiations to man to know whether alleles of this type are of common occurrence. Unfortunately, it is a problem of exceptional inherent difficulty, because we may expect that the more easily recognized genes will largely be among those with notably detrimental effects; and, conversely, that the conditionally advantageous genes will be mainly among those with minor effects and may, for just this reason, be difficult to recognize.

At this point I find it necessary to voice some misgivings which I have felt for a long time about one aspect of what might be called "genetical public relations". Soon after Muller's demonstration that X-rays have a mutagenic action, it was realized that they present a genetic hazard to man. At that time genes were thought of as consisting mainly, if not entirely, of common, advantageous, wild-type alleles and rare, deleterious, mutant alleles. They were unconditionally good or bad. Mutation was viewed as a necessary evil; it was something which happened, without which the species would lack the heritable variation on which future evolution depends, but it introduced into the population a load of mutant alleles which had to be eliminated by processes of natural selection. Each mutational event implied the occurrence of another mutant allele to be eliminated sooner or later through the "genetic death" of some individual if equilibrium were to be maintained.

I do not think anyone seriously doubts that this is a reasonably accurate representation of the state of affairs in respect of grossly deleterious autosomal dominant or sex-linked genes such as retinoblastoma or haemophilia. On the other hand, I think many geneticists would now doubt whether this concept is valid for more than a relatively small proportion of all human genes. Clear-cut, unconditionally deleterious oligogenes may be relative rarities. They may represent only one tail of a distribution; numerically, they may come far behind the polygenes, each with an effect so small as to be virtually undetectable by the methods of classical genetics, yet together of major importance because they regulate the quantitatively variable characteristics of each species through which evolution must largely operate. Now the outstanding feature of almost any quantitative character is that it has a central optimum; the extremes in either direction appear to be at a disadvantage, in respect of biological fitness, compared with some intermediate phenotype. The theoretical interpretation is that heterozygotes for genes affecting a quantitative character have a greater biological fitness than the corresponding homozygotes; and this implies that the mutation rate may be relatively unimportant in determining the gene frequency.

The above argument has been based mainly on theoretical considerations; but there is now a great mass of observational and experimental evidence that heterozygosity is the rule rather than the exception in wild populations. If anyone doubts it, he should re-read the writings of Dobzhansky and his co-workers on wild *Drosophila* populations, of Bruce Wallace on irradiated *Drosophila* populations and of Dunn on mouse populations; or he should try inbreeding any species that is normally cross-bred.

In the face of all this it is disconcerting to find that geneticists, when writing for the public, still often base their argument on an assertion that all mutation (or very nearly all) is harmful. I make this statement in the full knowledge that I myself use exactly the same argument when, as happens all too often nowadays, I have to give a talk on radiation hazards to an intelligent but genetically uninstructed audience. Perhaps its attraction is that it is a relatively easy argument to put over; or perhaps it is used because one can draw quantitative inferences about the genetic load due to some unconditionally deleterious human alleles, whereas at present it is almost impossible to speak quantitatively about human polygenic characters. But, whatever the reason, it is extremely important that geneticists should not blind themselves to the fact that unconditionally deleterious oligogenes may constitute only a small fraction of the human genome.

The necessity for using an argument such as this stems essentially from one fact: we know something about mutation in man and experimental animals, but we know very little about the effect on a population in which mutation is induced. We know enough to be reasonably certain that the current theory of Mendelian populations is over-simplified and unable to accomodate some essential features of real populations; but we have not yet got a satisfactory theory to put in its place. For the present there can be only one corollary; we must have more research on the genetic structure of populations, in the hope that the nature of the facts will become clearer and will stimulate the development of a more complete theory. This theory would have to cover the origin and loss of variation in populations: its origin by spontaneous or artificially enhanced mutation and by environmental action, and its loss by natural or artificial selection.

There have been many genetic studies of wild populations. Although in most of them the object was to study the effects of natural selection, it is only rarely that direct evidence has been obtained that the effect observed really was due to this cause. For example, the spread of melanic forms of various species of moths in industrial areas has been observed for over a century; and it has been assumed throughout that the spread was due to a selective advantage of the melanic form, following an environmental change from the relatively clean agricultural to the sooty industrial economy; but it was only last year that Kettlewell [6] was able to confirm the validity of this assumption, by direct observation of the numbers of moths of the various phenotypes taken by bird predators. It has also been a characteristic of studies of wild populations that, with few exceptions, the material studied has been polymorphic. This must have been due largely to subjective selection by the investigator, since a polymorphic population holds an obvious interest which a monomorphic population lacks. Nevertheless, where an apparently monomorphic population has been sufficiently closely observed, it has often proved to be polymorphic, even though the polymorphism may have been cryptic. Obvious examples are the populations of various *Drosophila* species studied by Dobzhansky and his school (see Wallace [11]), and the mouse populations studied by Dunn. [4] Dunn's work is of especial interest, because it shows that mechanisms whereby coadapted blocks of genes could come into existence are not peculiar to *Drosophila*. The mechanism in the mouse differs from that in *Drosophila*, but the effects are the same: suppression of crossing over and selective advantage of the heterozygous genotype in which it has been suppressed, even at the cost of a high proportion of inviable homozygotes. His findings gain significance in the light of the recent demonstration by my colleague Dr Mary Lyon, using an induced translocation, that the region of suppressed crossing over is at least five times as long as the short segment marked in Dunn's experiments.

The study of mutation and artificial selection in the laboratory and of natural selection in wild populations are three approaches to a much more difficult study—namely, that of populations with mutation rates that have been enhanced by ionizing radiations or other mutagens. Nor must it be forgotten that ionizing radiations have other genetic effects besides mutagenesis; they increase crossing over, a fact which was known before their mutagenic action was discovered and which may be of great importance in the study of polygenic systems.

So far, few have attempted to work with irradiated animal populations. History dictated that one of the first studies in this field should be of a human population; but the genetical work of the Atomic Bomb Casualty Commission was almost foredoomed to failure, in the sense that it was very unlikely that statistically significant observations could have been made, even on the basis of the most extreme assumption, namely, that all human "spontaneous" mutation is really induced by background radiation and that the doubling dose for man is consequently as low as 3 or 4 r. In the event the results were, with one possible exception, negative; but all who are concerned with planning human radiation genetic studies in the future will owe a debt to Neel and his colleagues for doing the pioneer work in this field and exposing some of the problems (Neel et al. [8]). The only other genetic studies of irradiated human populations of which I am aware are those of Crow [3] and of Macht & Lawrence; [7] in each case the irradiated population consisted of radiologists. Here also the results were, in the main, negative; and the work suffered from the further limitation that it was impossible to estimate, even roughly, the radiation dose received.

There remain the experimental studies of irradiated animal populations. Of these there have been exceptionally few; and in almost all the experimental material has been *Drosophila melanogaster*. There are two reasons for this: first, a population to be maintained under known irradiation conditions must almost of necessity be kept in the laboratory; secondly, to guard against the possible effects of genetic drift, the effective breeding population should be at least of several hundred individuals. These requirements of laboratory culture and population size can be reconciled only by limiting the size of the individual animal. Subject to this limitation, *D. melanogaster* is the obvious choice, being exceptionally well known genetically. We hope to develop techniques at Harwell for maintaining mouse populations in the laboratory, but I am doubtful whether it would be feasible to keep free-living populations of larger animals in an irradiated space. A possible solution might be to find an isolated wild colony and irradiate its habitat; this procedure would have the inherent defect, however, that one could not be sure of obtaining a truly comparable control population; and in this work controls are a *sine qua non*.

If anything were needed to show how wide is the gap between observational fact and existing population genetic theory, the few published studies of irradiated *Drosophila* populations would do it. The various writers have given up any attempt to interpret their observations in terms of gene frequencies, contenting themselves with observing what happens in their populations and attempting to interpret their observations in terms appropriate to the polygenic systems studied. Various combinations of selection type and mutational status have been used, and various types of foundation population. Wallace [10] has observed the effects of natural selection on biological fitness in populations originally derived from an inbred strain, but now heterogeneous, which were exposed to various levels of acute and chronic irradiation. Buzzati-Traverso [1] likewise observed the effects of natural selection in irradiated populations; but here the foundation populations were inbred and the effects observed were egg-production and the incidence of the *non-spineless* phenotype due to modification of the genetic milieu in a homozygous *spineless* population. Clayton & Robertson [2] likewise used inbred foundation populations; they observed the variance of the number of abdominal bristles and the response to artificial selection for this character. Scossiroli [9] selected for sternopleural hairs in an irradiated population which was genetically heterogeneous, but which had previously been selected by Mather without irradiation and had reached a plateau.

It is too early to attempt to draw general conclusions from these experiments, but some things are clear. Buzzati-Traverso's work shows that irradiation of an inbred population can release genetic variability in a character such as egg-production, which is one of the components of biological fitness, and can thereby enable natural selection to increase fitness. Scossiroli's work shows that irradiation can release genetic variability in a heterogeneous population which has reached a selection limit, and can thereby enable the limit to be surpassed. Wallace's work shows that populations can live successfully under conditions of irradiation in which a large proportion of their chromosomes carry gene combinations which are lethal when homozygous, but that some of these combinations may be advantageous when heterozygous. The work of Clayton & Robertson shows that the amount of genetic variability arising spontaneously through new mutation in each generation is only a minute fraction, perhaps a thousandth, of that normally present in a *Drosophila* population; and that a part only of the additional genetic variability released by irradiation may be available for selection.

Just what the full implications are for human genetics it is impossible at present to assess; but two conclusions seem inescapable:

1.   It is essential to extend work of this type and to cover other species, including mammals, with a much lower reproductive potential than *Drosophila*; the results might be very different in species where the female produced only ten young instead of hundreds, and selection differentials were consequently lower.

2.   We have no mandate from experimental fact to extend to the whole human genome the theoretical treatment of the genetic hazard of radiations that we now apply with a fair measure of confidence to grossly deleterious

gene mutations. It follows that for the present we must limit quantitative assessment to this part of the hazard alone; and this implies that the first task of human genetics must be to identify as completely as possible that part of the social load which is due to genes in this class.

REFERENCES

1. Buzzati-Traverso, A. (1954) *On the role of mutation rate in evolution.* In: *Proceedings of the Ninth International Congress of Genetics (Caryologia (Torino),* Suppl.), p. 450
2. Clayton, G. & Robertson, A. (1955) *Amer. Nat.,* **89,** 151
3. Crow, J. F. (1955) *Amer. J. Roentgenol.,* **73,** 467
4. Dunn, L. C. (1953) *Acta genet. (Basel),* **4,** 139
5. Fahmy, O. G. & Fahmy, M. J. (1956) *J. Genet.,* **54,** 146
6. Kettlewell, H. B. D. (1955) *Heredity,* **9,** 323
7. Macht, S. H. & Lawrence, P. S. (1955) *Amer. J. Roentgenol.,* **73,** 442
8. Neel, J. V. et al. (1953) *Science,* **118,** 537
9. Scossiroli, R. E. (1954) *I.U.B.S. Publ., Series B,* **15,** 42
10. Wallace, B. (1952) *Evolution,* **6,** 333
11. Wallace, B. (1954) *I.U.B.S. Publ., Series B,* **15,** 67

SOME OF THE PROBLEMS ACCOMPANYING AN INCREASE OF MUTATION RATES IN MENDELIAN POPULATIONS

Bruce WALLACE

The Biological Laboratory,
Cold Spring Harbor, Long Island, N.Y., USA

Problems arising from the exposure of man to irradiation are extremely numerous. They bear on many aspects of his health and his children's health. To the extent that the original exposure—medical or industrial—aims at improving man's welfare, he benefits; to the extent, however, that the exposure does him bodily harm or induces gene mutations that will harm his offspring, he suffers.

The mutagenic effects of radiation pose problems of immediate concern to the geneticist. These problems are of three major types: the development of a theory of population genetics adequate for the formulation of predictions; the design of experiments capable of testing the theory and of supplying empirical values for various parameters; and the extrapolation of theory and experimental results to human populations.

The postulated role of mutations in Mendelian populations depends largely upon the basic concept one entertains regarding the genetic structure of populations. In the main, there are two contrasting but not mutually exclusive concepts: the first is based upon the superiority of homozygous individuals; the second, upon the superiority of heterozygotes.

The first concept postulates that individuals of the highest possible fitness are completely homozygous. Natural selection acting within a constant environment would favour these individuals and would tend to establish a population composed entirely of homozygous individuals. In such a population the individuals of each generation should, ideally, be identical, and the individuals of one generation should be identical with those of the next. Mutations in a population such as this operate to frustrate the aims of natural selection. By definition, the new mutations are deleterious and, consequently, their constant formation prevents the population from reaching the level of fitness theoretically possible. Furthermore, under equilibrium conditions, the deleterious effect of mutations on the population is a function of mutation rates and is independent of the harm done to any one individual by any one mutation. Theoretical treatments of this problem have been given by Haldane,[2] by

Crow,[1] and, in great detail, by Muller.[6] Although no one actually believes that environmental conditions are constant or that the ideal population described above actually exists, the model is nevertheless reasonable if one assumes that near-equilibrium conditions exist at any moment and that genetic changes within populations occur slowly (see, for instance, Haldane [4]).

The second concept assumes that even under constant environmental conditions the individual with the highest fitness is genetically heterozygous rather than homozygous. Furthermore, there need not be one ideal genotype, but many. An ideal population of this sort would consist of individuals as phenotypically uniform as possible consistent with the demands of natural selection, but these individuals would be genetically diverse. Similarly, individuals of one generation would not be genetically identical, even under ideal conditions, with those of the next. The selective coefficient of any gene in this type of population would be a function of the genetic situation prevailing within that population. Since the population consists of individuals of diverse genotypes, selection would be constantly shuffling gene frequencies and selective values, simply because of the uncertainties associated with the formation of chance gene combinations. The details of this model have not been developed in a way comparable with the first; one can say, however, that gene frequencies under this model are primarily a function of selection and only secondarily a function of mutation rates.

These two concepts are not mutually exclusive. It may develop that one or the other is substantially correct. It may be that for some loci one is correct while for others the second applies. It is quite probable that different species differ in their genetic structure. Finally, at different times and in different places the genetic structure of a population may shift from one model to the other.

A few remarks may be made regarding the logic underlying these two concepts of population structure. Genes and chromosomes are the means by which information is passed from one generation to the next. In some cases they are the only means; in others this hereditary information is supplemented by the "spoken" word, which allows individuals of one generation to communicate with those of the next. The first concept, that based on the superiority of homozygous individuals, stresses the accuracy of the transmitted information. In the absence of mutations and of environmental change, every individual of a generation would be supplied with precisely that information which has proved valuable in the past. There is no wastage through the formation of ill-adapted individuals. Furthermore, it is a moral system in that, under ideal conditions, every individual is his neighbour's equal. The second concept entails wastage; certain individuals must obtain hereditary information that is not perfectly accurate. In so far as this wastage can be equated with suffering (and it certainly can be considered in this way for human beings), the second concept is morally deficient.

What arguments, then, can be mustered to support the second concept and to justify giving it serious consideration? First, to the extent that genes are semi-dominant, their frequencies are changed much more rapidly by the action of selection on heterozygous individuals than by that on rare homozygotes. Secondly, a gene that is beneficial through some semi-dominant effect need not be beneficial when homozygous; the nature of these homozygous individuals is unimportant to the population at the time selection favours the heterozygotes. Thirdly, the replacement of superior aa' individuals by equally good $a''a''$ individuals requires that the allele a'' also be advantageous when heterozygous. Fourthly, there are physiological reasons for doubting in some instances whether a single allele in homozygous individuals can actually duplicate the action of two contrasting alleles in heterozygotes.

One difficulty confronting the second concept is more apparent than real. It arises from the geneticist's inability to distinguish which of two alleles is a favourable dominant and which is a deleterious recessive (see Crow,[1] footnote to p. 285). A geneticist can detect gene effects by substitution only. Genetic changes within a population are determined by the sequence in which mutations occur. By completely ignoring the sequence of genetic change and by regarding the favourable dominant as "normal", one is forced to the absurd conclusion that the origin of each favourable dominant (or semi-dominant) lowers the fitness of the population and that the population regains its normal fitness only if the new dominant attains fixation in the population.

Finally, in reference to the first concept, the writer has mental reservations that stem from the assumed independence of the effect of the gene mutation on the population and the effect of the gene on individuals of the population. In other words, no matter how slight the deviation from the "normal" allele, the effect of a given class of mutant alleles is said to be proportional to mutation rate alone. In fact, Muller [5] mentions the possibility that small harmful mutations may be even worse for the population than fully lethal ones. The writer does not question the calculations that demonstrate this fact; he questions the assumptions upon which the calculations are based and which result in a curve with an abrupt break, regardless of how infinitesimal the effect of the mutation might be.

The problems mentioned so far lie in the realm of theoretical speculation. They are problems one meets when attempting to visualize techniques employed by Mendelian populations in meeting the demands of existence, techniques compatible with the known facts of genetics. The second large class of problems arises in connexion with the design of experiments aimed at testing the validity of theoretical models. Regardless of one's concept of the genetic structure of a population, obtaining experimental data to verify the concept or to furnish evidence regarding certain parameters is an overwhelming chore.

Information required for the manipulation of equations under the model that stresses homozygosity includes estimations of numbers of loci, total mutation rates, distributions of mutations in terms of their effects on various components of fitness (viability and fertility in particular), the distribution of deleterious mutations among individuals of a population, and dominance-recessive relationships. Information along these lines is being gathered at the Oak Ridge National Laboratory, Tenn., USA, and at the University of Indiana, under the direction of Dr Russell and of Professor Muller, respectively, as well as at a number of other laboratories. The writer feels sure that all geneticists will appreciate the tremendous effort required to obtain this information.

In our laboratory we have taken what appears superficially to be a somewhat simpler approach: the simultaneous analysis of the genetic content of experimental populations of *Drosophila melanogaster* in terms of genes affecting fitness and measures of fitness itself. The latter measure will be required for the final verification of one's concept of population structure regardless of which of the two one entertains. The chief difficulties in this approach lie in the estimation of fitness and in determining the amount of selection required to maintain this fitness. These difficulties are compounded by the necessity to limit one's studies to components of fitness and to carry out the analyses outside the population, outside even an experimental population. In studies of components of fitness one generally assumes that these components are to some degree correlated with one another and with their sum. Robertson [7] has pointed out, though, that in a population at genetic equilibrium the components of fitness must be negatively correlated. This indicates that a technique for measuring total fitness must eventually be found if the role of mutations in populations is to be evaluated experimentally.

Difficulties associated with the determination of selection pressures within populations do not seem insurmountable at the moment. Specific genetic changes within populations offer one source of information—for instance, the increase in frequency of one particular mutation, the establishment of equilibrium frequencies, or the loss of mutations following the cessation of irradiation. Estimations of population size shed light on the extent of inter-progeny selection; that is, one can judge whether a population exists because a few parents leave many offspring or because many parents leave a few each. Furthermore, larval mortality rates can be altered substantially without changing the adult population size to any appreciable extent; manipulations of this sort will offer an approach to the study of intra-progeny selection.

The final group of problems deals with the extrapolation of theory and experimental findings to man. The first problem that comes to mind is the shift in emphasis demanded by the importance of man's intellect.   In experimental material, "fitness" is equated with the ability to live and to reproduce;   the emphasis in eugenic studies on the differential fertility existing in relation to IQ and racial origins shows that the experimental concept of fitness is not completely acceptable for human populations. Furthermore, although a long life and a full life is highly desirable, length *per se* is not all-important.   Although the pertinent facts lie outside the realm of genetics, the writer suspects that the change from a 60-hour to a 40-hour working week has added more pleasurable, livable years to the average working man's life than he has lost by way of industrial and automobile accidents.   These and similar problems are concerned with values;   although there may be a consensus of opinion regarding these matters, there are bound to be sharp disagreements between societies and persons and even sharp changes in the views held by the same individual at different times.

Additional problems arise, too, because man is a social animal.   The two concepts of populations described earlier dealt with ideal individuals with the highest possible fitness;   these concepts are applicable to populations in which, with the exception of mating, there is no interaction between individuals in determining the fitness of the population.   Such concepts are inadequate for dealing with populations of social organisms in which the fitness of the population is a function not only of the fitness of the individual members but also of the interaction between individuals. It would seem that before one can approach the problem of the ideal genetic architecture of populations of social organisms, including man, one would have to solve the simpler problem of the ideal constellation of phenotypes. The writer does not recall having seen such an analysis for human populations.

The next problems to be discussed concern what may be described as experimental human ecology.   The central problem concerns the extent by which the visible human population, or, better, the reproducing human population, differs from the initial population of fertilized eggs from which it came.   How strong are the selective forces operating within human populations?   Mortality figures are available for the post-natal and late pre-natal periods.   Figures are undoubtedly available, too, for the proportion of individuals who remain childless throughout life.   Good data concerning the mortality of individuals in the early post-fertilization periods are not available at the moment.   Lacking, too, are indications of the extent to which this mortality and sterility (effective, if not actual, sterility) are selective; random elimination, of course, is ineffective in bringing about genetic changes within populations.   Haldane [3] has developed a method for estimating the intensity of selection that utilizes phenotypic measurements only;   this method may prove valuable in the analysis of human populations.   Other data that would shed light on the selective potentialities of human populations are those dealing with the rapidity with which resistance to certain diseases has spread within memory of man and the effectiveness of this newly acquired resistance; this information would need to include the price in terms of mortality that the affected populations paid while selection operated. Along these same lines, it would be of particular interest to determine the factors responsible for limiting the number of children per couple in many human societies. When the average number of offspring per pair falls irrevocably below two for any species, that species can no longer replace itself numerically from one generation to the next, and extinction is inevitable. In some human communities the present average is but slightly above two. Since this average is determined by a combination of sociological and biological factors, some effort should be expended to determine the actual biological limit for the number of offspring human couples can have.

If selection should turn out to be more effective in man than we have suspected, we must nevertheless be wary of those who claim that radiation will do no harm to the human species. The rate at which mutant genes enter the gene pool of a population must equal the rate at which they leave. Mutant genes leave the gene pool by the effective elimination of individuals either through death, sterility, failure to reproduce, or a tendency to reproduce at a reduced rate. Effective elimination of individuals means, for human beings, that one individual is placed at a disadvantage relative to another; in many instances the "elimination" is accompanied by mental or physical suffering. Therefore, regardless of the ability or inability of "natural" selection within human populations to forestall extinction or to maintain the "fitness" of the population as a whole, we are still forced to the conclusion that every exposure of individuals to irradiation must be justifiable in terms of the beneficial effects that exposure confers either to the exposed individual or to the population as a whole. In the light of the known effects of radiation, it is essential that accidental or unnecessarily high exposures be avoided.

REFERENCES

1. Crow, J. F. (1952) *Dominance and overdominance*. In: Gowen, J. S., ed., *Heterosis*, Ames, Iowa, p. 282
2. Haldane, J. B. S. (1937) *Amer. Nat.*, **71**, 337
3. Haldane, J. B. S. (1954) *The measurement of natural selection*. In: *Proceedings of the Ninth International Congress of Genetics (Caryologia (Torino)*, Suppl.), p. 480
4. Haldane, J. B. S. (1954) *The statics of evolution*. In: Huxley, J., Hardy, A. C. & Ford, E. B., ed., *Evolution as a process*, London, p. 109
5. Muller, H. J. (1948) *Bull. N.Y. Acad. Med.*, **24**, 447
6. Muller, H. J. (1950) *Amer. J. hum. Genet.*, **2**, 111
7. Robertson, A. (1956) *Cold Spr. Harb. Symp. quant. Biol.*, **20**, 225

EXPOSURE OF MAN TO IONIZING RADIATIONS, WITH SPECIAL REFERENCE TO POSSIBLE GENETIC HAZARDS

R. M. SIEVERT

Institute of Radiophysics, Karolinska Hospital,
Stockholm, Sweden

The purpose of this review is to show which generally occurring sources of ionizing radiation may at present be relevant and which irrelevant in discussing the effects of ionizing radiations on man.

We have to consider the direct effects on human tissues, as well as the indirect effects due to mutations of somatic cells or of germ cells. Mutations of the former cells do harm to the individual himself. Mutations of the germ cells may involve risks for the offspring as early as the next generation, consequently being of interest to the individual himself, or may—in the case of irradiation of a large number of inhabitants—constitute a long-term problem in the entire population.

The present sources of ionizing radiations which are of interest in connexion with the effects just mentioned include the following:

Natural sources of radiation

(*a*) Sources of cosmic radiation.

(*b*) The natural radioactive elements, particularly radium, thorium and potassium, in the earth's crust.

(*c*) The natural content of radioactive elements in man.

Man-made sources of radiation

(*a*) Radioactive material and technical arrangements producing radiation (X-ray tubes, other particle accelerators and nuclear reactors) used under such circumstances that the user is generally aware of the presence of the radiation (e.g., used in education, science, medicine and industry).

(*b*) Sources of radiation used for purposes in which, as a rule, only the specialist is aware of the presence of ionizing radiation (e.g., radioactive luminous compounds on watches and other articles for common use, television sets, etc.).

(*c*) Artificial radioactive elements distributed by man in nature.

Maximum Permissible Levels of Ionizing Radiation for Individuals and Large Populations

Before describing the different sources of radiation which contribute to a larger or smaller extent in producing the present level of ionizing radiation in man, a brief account of the maximum permissible doses recommended may be given.

The International Commission on Radiological Protection (ICRP) at its session in Geneva, in April 1956, decided to make the following additions to their earlier recommendations:

"A *controlled* area is one in which the occupational exposure of personnel to radiation or radioactive material is under the supervision of a radiation safety officer.

"For such personnel the maximum permissible levels of exposure are those specified for occupational exposure.   In the case of prolonged exposure to radiation from external sources the maximum permissible levels for occupational exposure are represented by weekly doses of 600 mrem in the skin and 300 mrem in the blood-forming organs, the gonads and the lenses of the eyes."

* * *

"For any person in any place outside of controlled areas the maximum permissible levels of exposure are 10 % of the occupational exposure levels."

* * *

"When genetic aspects of the effects of radiation are considered, the dose received by the whole population is of importance.   Scientific data derived from human as distinct from experimental animal populations are so scanty that no precise permissible dose for a population can, at present, be set.   The available information is being assessed by the Commission and other groups including geneticists.   Until general agreement is reached, it is prudent to limit the dose of radiation received by gametes from all sources additional to the natural background to an amount of the order of the natural background in presently inhabited regions of the earth."

* * *

"The recommended maximum permissible weekly doses and the modified values for special circumstances, permit a desirable degree of flexibility for their application.   In practice it has been found that in order not to exceed these maximum limits and also to comply with the general recommendations of the Commission 'that exposure to radiation be kept at the lowest practicable level in all cases' a considerable factor of safety must be allowed in the design of protective devices and operating procedures.   Therefore, under present conditions, it is expected that the average yearly occupational dose actually received by an occupationally exposed person would be about 5 rems and the accumulated dose in the employment period up to 30 years of age would be about 50 rems. Accordingly, the Commission recommends continuation of the present conservative practice as regards doses actually received by occupationally exposed personnel, to keep the accumulated dose as low as practicable especially up to age 30."

In the report of the Medical Research Council of Great Britain (MRC) [3] "The Hazards to Man of Nuclear and Allied Radiations", issued in June 1956, the following conclusions are drawn:

" 2.   *Dose levels to the individual*

(*a*)   In conditions involving persistent exposure to ionizing radiations, the present standard, recommended by the International Commission on Radiological Protection, that the dose received shall not exceed 0.3 r weekly, averaged over any period of 13 consecutive weeks, should, for the present, continue to be accepted.

(*b*) During his whole lifetime, an individual should not be allowed to accumulate more than 200 r of *whole-body* radiation, in addition to that received from the natural background, and this allowance should be spread over tens of years, but every endeavour should be made to keep the level of exposure as low as possible.

(*c*) An individual should not be allowed to accumulate more than 50 r of radiation *to the gonads*, in addition to that received from the natural background, from conception to the age of 30 years; and this allowance should not apply to more than one-fiftieth of the total population of this country.

" 3. *Dose level to the population*
Those responsible for authorising the development and use of sources of ionizing radiation should be advised that the upper limit, which future knowledge may set to the total dose of extra radiation which may be received by the population as a whole, is not likely to be more than twice the dose which is already received from the natural background; the recommended figure may indeed be appreciably lower than this." [3] (p. 80)

In the report of the US National Academy of Sciences (NAS) [11] "The Biological Effects of Atomic Radiation", the following recommendations are made:

"C) That for the present it be accepted as a uniform national standard that X-ray installations (medical and nonmedical), power installations, disposal of radioactive wastes, experimental installations, testing of weapons, and all other humanly controllable sources of radiations be so restricted that members of our general population shall not receive from such sources an average of more than 10 roentgens, in addition to background, of ionizing radiation as a total accumulated dose to the reproductive cells from conception to age 30."

* * *

"E) That individual persons not receive more than a total accumulated dose to the reproductive cells of 50 roentgens up to age 30 years (by which age, on the average, over half of the children will have been born), and not more than 50 roentgens additional up to age 40 (by which time about nine tenths of their children will have been born)." [11] (p. 29)

Evidently it is generally agreed that at present it is desirable to limit the doses received by the gonads of individuals to less than 5 roentgens (r) per year and 50 r before 30 years of age, and that the average dose to the gonads of the population as a whole should be kept very low: of the order of the natural background (ICRP); twice this level (MRC); and 10 r before 30 years of age (NAS). The difference in these figures is not very important as their order of magnitude will in practice be about the same.

According to our present knowledge it seems likely that a dose of 30-80 r will (according to MRC) double the natural mutation rate in man, which is probably only to a minor fraction (perhaps about 10%) caused by ionizing radiations. The rest of the natural mutations will, to an unknown extent, be due to chemicals and to the thermal movements of the molecules. It seems to be highly desirable for the mutations induced by chemicals in particular to be investigated, in order to elucidate the relative role of radiation-induced mutations.

5

The recommendations made by the organizations quoted above are as regards the whole population based mainly on the natural level of ionizing radiation. It is not the place here to discuss whether this is a correct starting-point, nor whether or not the maximum permissible dose levels recommended are reasonable. They have been fixed after careful consideration based on our present, unfortunately very incomplete, knowledge of the biological effects of small radiation doses, but have been agreed to by specialists in biology, genetics, haematology, physics, and radiology with long experience in radiation protection both on the research and on the practical side.

With respect to the risks of injurious effects on man, one matter may, however, be stressed. There must always be a reasonable ratio between what can be gained by the use of ionizing radiation and the risks of its injurious effects. The use in medicine of ionizing radiation for examination and treatment of patients therefore occupies an exceptional position, which has not always been taken into account in recent years, in the discussion of the problems of the general irradiation of mankind. There must certainly be a sound balance between the benefits of a good health service and the risks to the patients with respect to onset of malignant disease or genetic damage of which, however, we at present do not know very much.

Natural Sources of Ionizing Radiations

Cosmic radiation

The cosmic radiations produce the doses shown in Table I.

The values for 0-4000 m have been calculated from the work of Compton and co-workers (Fig. 1), taking into consideration that some reduction due to absorption may be justified indoors, and the values for 6000-18000 m from Millikan and co-workers (Fig. 2). The values are

TABLE I. ROUGHLY ESTIMATED DOSES IN SOFT TISSUE FROM COSMIC RADIATION, EXPRESSED IN RAD PER THIRTY YEARS

Geomagnetic latitude	Dose, in rad, at an altitude above sea level, in metres, of						Hours per week to accumulate a dose of 50 rem during 10 years at 18 000 m
	0*	2 000*	4 000*	6 000**	12 000**	18 000**	
0°	0.7	1.1	2.0	8	35	40 (400) †	63
40°	0.8	1.3	2.5	12	70	110 (1100)†	25
60°	0.8	1.4	2.7	14	85	150 (1500)†	17

* Calculated from the measurements of A. H. Compton and co-workers (see Halliday[4]).
** Calculated from the measurements of R. A. Millikan and co-workers (see Schaefer[7]).
† The figures in brackets are estimated values in rem, assuming an RBE of 10.

FIG. 1. COSMIC RADIATION AT VARIOUS ALTITUDES,
ACCORDING TO COMPTON AND CO-WORKERS

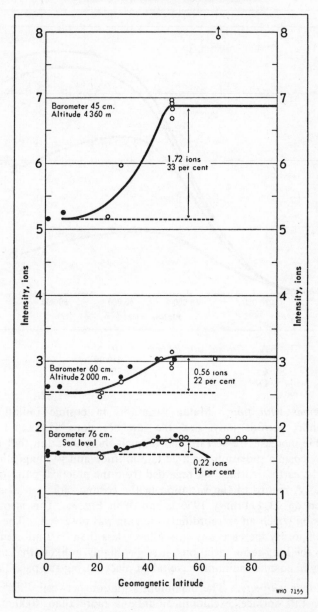

fairly approximate, as there are many factors which are difficult to allow
for at the higher altitudes, especially with regard to the unknown relative
biological effectiveness of heavy nuclei rays.

FIG. 2.   COSMIC RADIATION AT HIGH ALTITUDES,
ACCORDING TO MILLIKAN AND CO-WORKERS

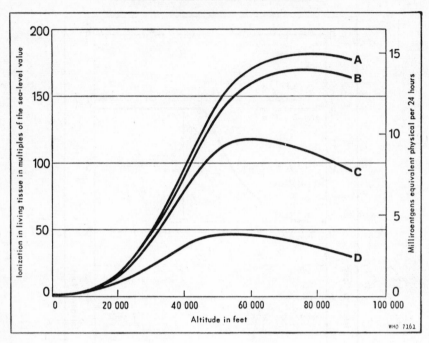

A.	Geomagnetic latitude	:	60° N
B.	,,	,,	:	51° N
C.	,,	,,	:	38° N
D.	,,	,,	:	3° N

Variations with time. Major variations in cosmic radiation occur during short periods only, and the few occasions associated with an appreciable increase are so rare and of such short duration that the doses caused by cosmic radiation for a certain altitude and geomagnetic latitude may, at the earth's surface, be regarded from the practical point of view as constant. A record of the variation in the cosmic radiation at six places in Sweden on 23 February 1956 is shown in Fig. 3. This is one of the occasions on which an extraordinary increase was observed. The dose due to this temporary increase was, at sea level, less than 0.03 millirem.

As to the long-term variations, it seems highly unlikely that any major variations in cosmic radiation have taken place during the past 2000 years.

Variations with site. The maximum variation between different places on the earth's surface, excluding mountains more than 4000 m high, is about 2 r per 30 years.

Doses to individuals. The doses to individuals may be of importance at very high altitudes. The present development of communication by air

FIG. 3(A). VARIATION IN COSMIC RADIATION AT ALTITUDE OF 50-500 METRES
ABOVE SEA LEVEL RECORDED IN FEBRUARY 1956 AT THE PLACES
I-VI SHOWN IN FIG. 3(B)

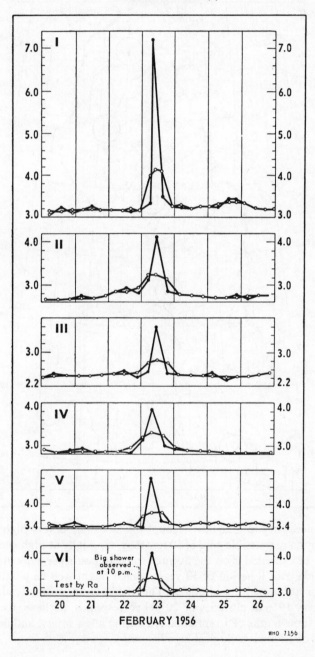

FIG. 3(B). SITE OF SWEDISH BACKGROUND-RADIATION RECORDING-STATIONS

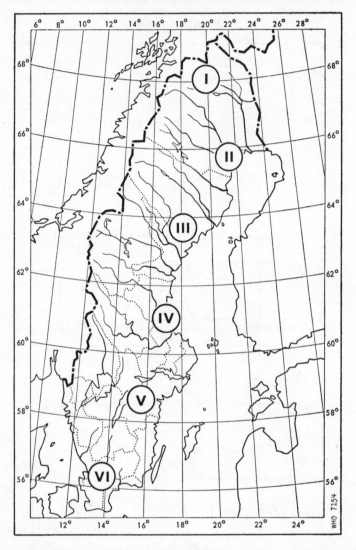

makes it necessary to take into account the fact that, at very high altitudes, the maximum permissible dose of 50 rem may, especially at high geomagnetic latitudes, be exceeded if on the average some 10 hours per week are spent at this altitude over a period of 10 years, which might well be possible in the future for personnel in aircraft. The increase in cosmic radiation on 23 February 1956 at altitudes of 20 000 corresponds, perhaps, to a dose of less than some tenths of 1 rem obtained during a few hours, and is therefore probably of limited biological significance.

Doses to large populations. The contribution to the irradiation of large population groups (> 100 000) varies between 0.7 and 2.7 r or approximately between 1 and 3 rem per 30 years.

The fact that an appreciable part of the radiation can be screened off by reasonable quantities of material may be of certain value for judging the risk for stratosphere and interstellar traffic. Investigations of the biological effects of cosmic radiation at very high altitudes are, however, desirable, because of the lack of knowledge as to the relative biological efficiency (RBE) values for heavy nuclei radiations.

Natural external γ-radiation

The external γ-radiation in nature varies with the radium, thorium, and potassium content of the ground and of the building material in houses. The γ-dose in free air produced above level ground can be calculated according to the simple formulae given below: [5]

Dose, in r, per 30 years

Radium	$0.57 \times 10^{12} \times s$ (Ra)
Uranium	$0.20 \times 10^6 \times s$ (U)
Thorium	$0.094 \times 10^6 \times s$ (Th)
Potassium	$41 \times s$ (K-39)

in which s (Ra), s (U), s (Th) and s (K-39), are the contents of radium, uranium, thorium, and potassium in g of element per g of ground substance.

To obtain an estimate of the dose to the gonads in rad,[a] the doses in free air have to be multiplied by a factor of 0.5 for women and 0.7 for men,[5] or on the average 0.6, to account for the absorption in the shielding part of the body. The same factor may be approximately applicable to most of the other organs. For the skeleton, the factor might be considered, on the average, to be about 0.8.

The doses due to natural γ-radiation over ground containing various minerals are given in Table II, and the doses in dwellings in Sweden [5] are seen from Table III and Fig. 4. These are in good agreement with the few observations which have been made in other countries.

The γ-radiation from the ground is absorbed by snow, as seen from Fig. 5. A snow cover of 40 cm depth and of medium volume and weight absorbs about 50% of the γ-radiation from the ground.

A factor of considerable importance is the relation between the time spent indoors and out of doors. Here, it is assumed that on an average in large population groups one quarter of the life is spent out of doors.

As an additional contribution to the irradiation of man from natural radioactive elements in the earth's crust, the radon and thoron of the air

---

a) 1 rad corresponds to a dose of about 1.07 r in soft tissue.

TABLE II. CALCULATED GONAD DOSES ABOVE VARIOUS MINERALS

Mineral	Ionization (ionpairs/cm³-sec) due to content of			Gonad dose (excludingcosmic radiation) in r per 30 years
	Ra	Th	K	
Igneous rocks				
Average	1.6	2.5	2.4	1.9
Granites:			3.2	
North America, Greenland	2.0	1.7		2.0
Finland	5.9	5.9		4.1
Alps	5.5	6.9		4.3
Basalts:			1.2	
North America, Greenland	1.2	2.1		1.2
England, Germany, France and Hungary	1.6	1.9		1.2
Sedimentary rocks				
Sandstone	0.4	1.0	0.9	0.8
Limestone	1.3	0.2	0.3	0.6
Alum shales in Sweden . .	75	0.3	3.2	21.0
Ore containing*				
1% U	—	—	—	1000
1% Th	—	—	—	500
0.01-0.001% Th**	—	—	—	0.5-5.0

* The uranium and thorium are in most cases very unevenly distributed and therefore the figures given here may be of limited practical value. According to a personal communication from Professor Z. M. Bacq, University of Liège, the background radiation in Katanga, Belgian Congo, will reach 100-150 times the normal background.
** Travancore sand, containing monazite, according to a personal communication from J. Eklund, Geological Survey of Sweden.

may play an important role in special cases. In general, the content of these elements in the air is too small to contribute to the dose received by the human body by more than a few per cent. In some places and during some periods, however, this content can be fairly high—for instance, in rooms where water of high radon concentration is used or the ventilation is insufficient,[5] in cellars where radon and thoron come up from the earth, and in large cities during calm weather.[1] Such cases seem only occasionally to have been investigated, and it would probably be worth while to make more systematic studies in this field. At present, these sources of natural radiation are too little known to be treated in this survey and will therefore be disregarded, although it is possible that they are of significance for the irradiation of the pulmonary system of a comparatively large number of individuals living in certain areas.

Variation with time. The average annual dose to human beings due to natural sources has probably remained roughly the same throughout the present geological period. A slight decrease in the radiation occurred when man learned to use wood for building houses, and stopped living in earthern huts or in rocks where the amount of radon in the air was sometimes probably quite high. The level subsequently increased again with the use

TABLE III. SUMMARY OF RESULTS OF GAMMA-RADIATION MEASUREMENTS
IN SWEDISH DWELLINGS*

Building material in outer walls	Mean gonad dose in r per 30 years		
	middle of room	highest value recorded	lowest value recorded
Wood	1.0	1.1	0.95
Brick	2.0	2.2	1.9
Light-weight concrete containing alum shale	3.2	3.8	3.0

* Calculated from Hultqvist's figures; [5] cosmic radiation excluded.

FIG. 4. DISTRIBUTION OF AVERAGE RADIATION IN SWEDISH DWELLINGS OF THREE TYPES

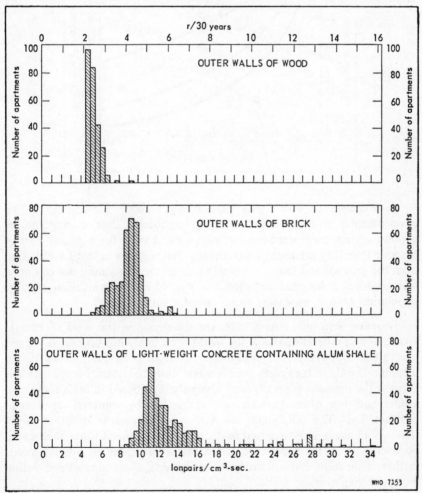

of bricks and concrete as building materials, and when people moved to cities, where the material surrounding them more frequently contains minerals.

FIG. 5.   DECREASE IN GAMMA-RADIATION WITH DEPTH OF SNOW COVER
AT THREE DIFFERENT SNOW DENSITIES

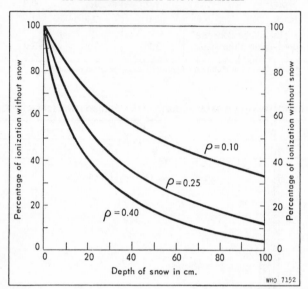

A circumstance which may have brought about a reduction in the environmental γ-radiation for some populations is that, during the ice periods, certain areas were covered with ice and snow for a greater part of the year than they are today. As already shown, snow absorbs γ-radiation from the ground, and thus appreciably reduces the irradiation out of doors, and produces a seasonal variation (see Fig. 6) in the irradiation of large population groups, especially those living in rural districts.

Variation with site. As a rule, the difference in the level of natural γ-radiation in different parts of the world is probably not very large. Even over areas containing rich uranium or thorium ores, the γ-doses to the inhabitants only in rare cases exceed a few times the normal level. This is because the ores are generally very unevenly distributed in both rocks and sands, and are often covered or surrounded by material of normal radioactivity. The inhabitants moving over the area in question might thus, on an average, be exposed to doses which are much lower than could be conceived. This experience based on observations in Sweden needs further verification, but will probably be found to apply to most population groups throughout the world.

The doses of γ-radiation to persons living in places more or less permanently covered with deep ice or snow, and to those spending most of their time at sea, are generally very small.   Here, the amount of γ-radiation

FIG. 6.   SEASONAL VARIATION IN GAMMA-RADIATION RECORDED AT FOUR PLACES
IN SWEDEN (I-IV IN FIG. 3(B)) AND CORRESPONDING SNOW COVER
PLOTTED AS NEGATIVE VALUES

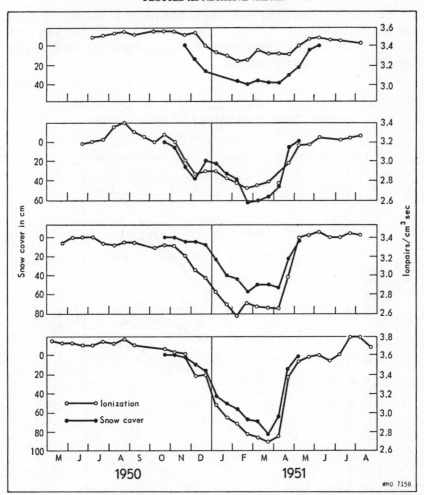

from the earth is often so minute that it can be entirely disregarded in comparison with the radiation from other natural sources. Recent investigations of the radiation level on wooden and iron vessels of different sizes have shown that the γ-radiation at a distance of only a few metres from a granite wharf is entirely negligible.

The results of investigations in Great Britain, Sweden and the USA have shown that the average values for the irradiation of large population groups due to natural sources in these three countries are as follows:

Great Britain. . . . . 2-3 rem per 30 years
Sweden . . . . 2-5 rem per 30 years
USA . . . . 4.3 rem per 30 years

In view of the statements made above with regard to the average doses received by individuals, it would be of interest to carry out long-term measurements by means of personal monitoring, in order to arrive at reliable data on the doses actually received.

FIG. 7. VARIATIONS IN GAMMA-RADIATION* FROM MALE AND FEMALE HUMAN SUBJECTS OF DIFFERENT AGES AND BODY-WEIGHTS

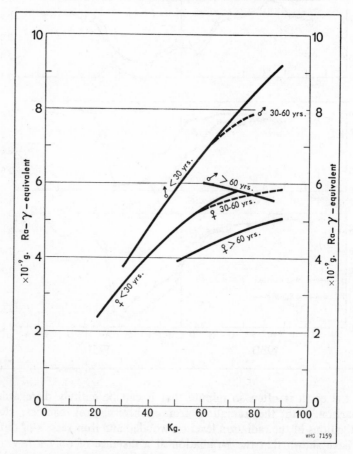

* More than 95% of the radiation is due to the potassium-40 content.

Natural content of radioactive elements in man

In areas where the radium content of drinking-water and food is not exceptionally high, the potassium content of human tissues is the main source of internal irradiation (see Fig. 7). The doses, in rad, due to the amount of potassium-40 (0.012% in natural potassium) in some human organs are shown in Table IV. With respect to some tissues, particularly bone, the data of different authors vary considerably.

TABLE IV. POTASSIUM CONTENT IN ADULT HUMAN SUBJECTS ACCORDING TO SHOHL[8] (A) AND FORBES & LEWIS[3] (B AND C) AND DOSE DUE TO K-40

Organ	Weight in % of whole body			% K-39			Dose in organ in r per 30 years (mean of B and C)
	A	B	C	A	B	C	
Skin	7.3	6.4	6.5	0.09	0.15	0.16	0.30
Skeleton . . .	17.5	17.5	14.7	0.055	0.10	0.11	0.20
Tibia	—	1.4	—	—	—	0.05	—
Muscle . . .	43.0	39.5	39.6	0.42	0.33	0.30	0.62
Nerve	—	3.0	2.1	—	0.28	0.29	0.56
Liver	2.7	2.3	2.3	0.17	0.27	0.22	0.49
Heart	0.5	0.5	0.6	0.13	0.22	0.19	0.40
Lungs	1.5	3.3	2.2	0.15	0.24	0.26	0.50
Kidneys . . .	0.5	0.5	0.4	0.17	0.16	0.22	0.38
GI. tract . . .	—	1.8	1.5	—	0.13	0.13	0.26
Adipose . . .	—	11.3	21.4	—	0.08	0.06	0.14
Remainder . .	—	11.3	6.4	—	0.18	0.17	0.34
Weight loss on dissection . .	—	2.6	2.2	—	—	—	—
Total body . . .	70 kg	53.8 kg	73.5 kg	0.205	0.212	0.190	0.40

The content of carbon-14 and radon contributes about 5% and 10%, respectively, of the average potassium radiation.

According to measurements made by Hursh & Gates [6] and recently by Sievert & Hultqvist [9] (Fig. 8), the radium content of the skeleton is probably less than 0.3×10^{-9} g, in areas with a radium content in the water of less than 0.2 μμg per litre. According to Spiers,[10] the mean dose to the osteocytes is about 6 rem per 30 years for 0.5×10^{-9} g of total radium body burden. The amount of radium is, however, very unevenly distributed in the skeleton, and the dose significant for the production of osteosarcoma therefore seems to be extremely difficult to assess.

The *variation with time and site* in the natural internal irradiation is mainly a question of the variations in the radium content of water and food and of the radon in the air. Referring to what has already been said, it may be stated that there are not at present sufficient data available to give

FIG. 8. COMPARISON OF WHOLE-BODY GAMMA-RADIATION OF MALE AND FEMALE PERSONS
IN VARIOUS AGE-GROUPS LIVING IN CITIES WITH DIFFERENT CONTENTS
OF RADIUM IN THE WATER-SUPPLY

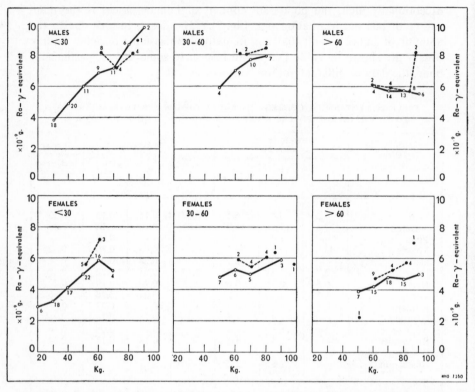

————— *0.2 μμg of Ra per litre of water*   - - - - - - - *1-2 μμg of Ra per litre of water*

any reliable figures for different areas in the world.   This also applies to the
problem of the natural radioactive elements taken up in the pulmonary
system.   With respect to these matters, reference can be made to a recent
publication by Hultqvist,[5] in which an extensive bibliography is given.

The common limits of the doses to large population groups (>100 000)
and to individuals from natural radiations are shown in Table V.

Man-made Sources of Ionizing Radiations

*Radioactive material and technical arrangements producing ionizing radiation
used under such circumstances that the user is generally aware of the
presence of the radiation*

Here, *occupational exposure* and *exposure of patients* undergoing
treatment or investigation in radiology are the two matters to be considered.

TABLE V. ESTIMATED VALUES FOR IRRADIATION OF THE GONADS OF THE POPULATION FROM NATURAL SOURCES EXPRESSED IN REM PER THIRTY YEARS

	For large population groups			For individuals	
	minimum	maximum	average	minimum	maximum
Cosmic radiation	0.7 (including screening in dwellings)	3? (at about 4000 m above sea level)	1?	0.5? (for some miners)	5? (50?)* (* 3% of 30 years spent at 18 000 m above sea level)
Natural radiation ¼ of 30 years out of doors	< 0.1 (above water, snow and ice)	1 (above igneous rocks)	0.5	0	15 (20?)
¾ of 30 years indoors	0.9 (in wooden houses)	3 (in some types of brick and concrete houses)	2		
Radon in air	0.03 (out of doors and in wooden houses with good ventilation) $(3 \times 10^{-13}c/1)$	0.8 (in cellars and in stone houses with poor ventilation) $(50 \times 10^{-13}c/1)$	0.2	<0.01 $(< 10^{-13}c/1)$	2.0 $(10^{-11}c/1)$
K-40 in body (+ 0.03 for C-14)	0.5	0.5	0.5	0.5	0.5
Approximate sum for gonads	2	6 (8?)	4	1	20 (> 50?)

The doses received by those carrying out work with ionizing radiation in education, science, medicine, and industry are in most cases small, as the personnel can generally be adequately protected. Furthermore, in all work where patients are not involved, there is no reason to permit irradiation which can in any way cause ill-effects. Here, the maximum permissible levels for individuals and large population groups are exceeded in rare cases only.

In radiology, especially some procedures in γ-ray therapy and in examinations using X-rays, circumstances do not always permit entirely satisfactory protection of doctors and personnel. Here, the individual dose will sometimes be close to the maximum permissible levels, and may even exceed them occasionally.

The occupational doses contribute to the radiation per capita of whole populations an amount which in Great Britain [3] has been estimated at about 2.5 r per year as an average for about 14 000 research, medical, and industrial workers, and at about 0.4 r per year for about 7 000 people engaged in atomic energy work. Altogether, the average gonad dose per capita due to occupational exposure is estimated at 0.0016 r per year; in other words, if 10 years is assumed to be the average period of work before reproduction, the relevant average gonad dose for the whole population may be less than 0.02 r before 30 years of age. An estimate of the corresponding figure for Sweden has given a considerably lower figure.

The occupational dose is apparently throughout the world attributed mainly to medical radiology, but the figures are presumably very uncertain. It seems, however, that occupational irradiation does not at present contribute any appreciable amount to the gonad dose of whole populations.

The doses received by patients undergoing treatment and examination by means of ionizing radiations, on the other hand, are of decisive importance, since they constitute by far the largest exposure of the population to man-made sources of radiation. In France, Germany, Great Britain, Sweden, and the USA, investigations have been carried out in order to ascertain the doses to patients during various types of radiological procedure. Numerous publications are available, but up to now estimations of the present average dose to the whole population due to the irradiation of patients have been made only in Great Britain, Sweden, and the USA. The results show that the average gonad dose per capita due to irradiated patients seems to be of the order of 1-3 r in 30 years. The reliability of these estimates has been much discussed, and it seems advisable to await further investigations, based on radiation measurements and some type of sampling method, before accepting any definite figures. It is nevertheless highly probable that the order of magnitude of the figures quoted is correct, since the estimations were made independently in three different countries.

Sources of radiation used for purposes in which, as a rule, only the specialist is aware of the presence of ionizing radiation

At present, we are faced in this field with only a few matters of minor significance. The average gonad dose from luminous compounds in watches is found in Great Britain [3] to contribute 0.01 r per year to the average gonad dose, and the radiation from television sets contributes a still more insignificant dose.

In the future development of atomic energy it seems highly probable, however, that the use of radioisotopes for various purposes will change the situation, and that the resultant distribution in the community of a large number of small radiation sources, each completely harmless individually, but collectively raising the level of irradiation of the population, will give rise to a new problem.

Artificial radioactive elements distributed in nature

The World Health Organization and its Study Group on the Effects of Radiation on Human Heredity are concerned with the peaceful uses of

FIG. 9.   GAMMA-RADIATION OBSERVED AT THE PLACES I-IV IN FIG. 3(B)
FIVE DAYS AFTER A DISTANT HYDROGEN-BOMB TEST

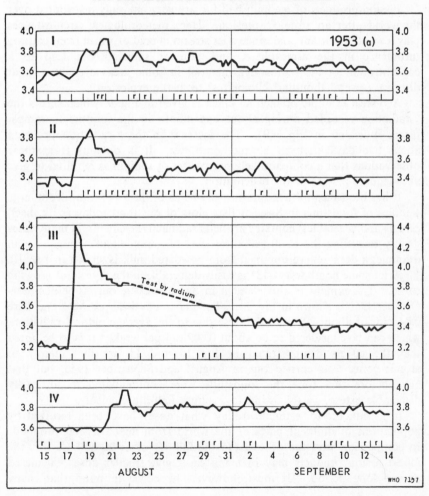

WHO 7197

atomic energy and the results of, for instance, the disposal of radioactive wastes from such uses.   However, it is essential to take into consideration here the evidence available from atomic-weapon tests, since the distribution of artificial radioactive elements in nature is, at present, mainly due to fall-out from these tests.   The dose due to external γ-radiation from fall-out may at the time of writing (December 1956) be disregarded in comparison with the internal dose.

Leaving aside the fall-out in the vicinity of the test area and the effects of radiation during the first few days after the explosion, two different effects may be of interest.   One is caused by mixed fission products with a medium half-life (a few days to less than one year), the other by the fission products with a long half-life, particularly Sr-90 (28 years) and Cs-137 (33 years).

Fission products of medium half-life are very unevenly distributed over the world after an atomic explosion.   Here, meteorological circumstances play a most important role, since a jet stream, a cold or warm front causing turbulence in the atmosphere, and rain or snowfall can lead to a concentration of the radioactive material in some areas even at a great distance (several thousand kilometres) from the explosion.

A typical example of such an effect is given in Fig. 9, which shows the γ-radiation recorded during about one month in the four northernmost places indicated in Fig. 3(B).   The increase in the γ-radiation occurred about five days after an atomic-bomb test.   It is obvious from these observations that a comparatively narrow set of stations is required to give an adequate picture of the distribution.

It has been shown by recent measurements of the γ-radiation from large samples of foodstuffs in Sweden that most of our food today (milk, beef, cereals and vegetables) contains artificial radioactive elements, in many cases greatly exceeding the K-40 radiation level of animals and plants.   As an example, a decay curve obtained from powdered milk is shown in Fig. 10.

After some bomb tests I-131 is easily detectable in the thyroid of growing cattle.   The content of this element in Swedish cattle during September - October 1956 is shown in Fig. 11.   The maximum dose per week was here 0.04 rad, or about 20 times the dose due to the average natural radiation, which can be considered to be about 0.002 rad per week.   It is to be noted that the effects demonstrated in Fig. 10 and 11 are due mainly to atomic-bomb tests carried out in August and September 1956, but that even before that time the foodstuffs were contaminated to an easily detectable extent, partly owing to medium half-life elements.

It is difficult to estimate today what doses have been received by populations in different parts of the world from mixed fission products. In comparison with the doses from the fall-out of Sr-90 and Cs-137, the mixed fission products may in many cases give smaller doses calculated over a long period.   It must, however, be borne in mind that many more biological effects may be dependent on the intensity of the radiation than we at present know. Our knowledge of the effects of small doses over long periods is very scanty and we cannot as yet be sure that the time-intensity factor can be disregarded, even with respect to genetic effects.

FIG. 10. DECAY CURVE FOR GAMMA-RADIATION FROM MIXED FISSION PRODUCTS IN POWDERED MILK

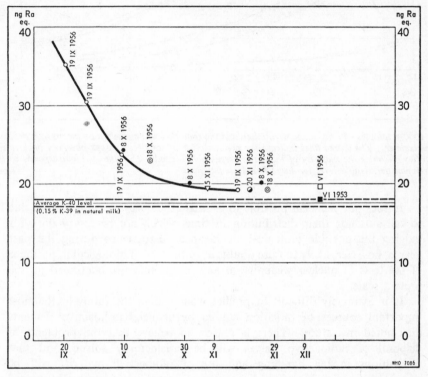

The sample of powdered milk was taken in September 1956 and the radiation was measured by means of a pressure ion-chamber.

The fall-out of Sr-90 and Cs-137 has been carefully studied during the past years. These elements are probably comparatively evenly distributed over the whole world (with the possible exception of the polar regions). At present, large amounts of them remain in the upper atmosphere, but they will gradually fall, and it is estimated that the present abundance of Sr-90 and Cs-137 on the earth's surface will eventually be increased by a factor of 3-5, even if the firing of atom bombs is stopped. The incorporation of Sr-90 into the skeleton may, in places where the calcium content of the soil is small, be regarded as important.

FIG. 11.　GAMMA-RADIATION FROM IODINE-131 IN THYROIDS FROM GRAZING CATTLE

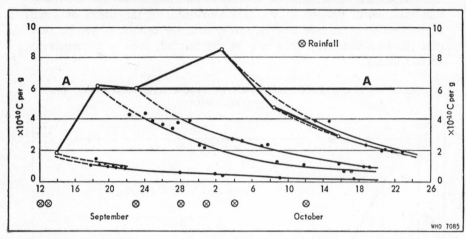

1000-g samples (50 thyroids) were taken and the radiation was measured by means of a pressure ion-chamber. The dotted lines indicate the extrapolation of the decay curves observed back to the last day on which the majority of the cattle presumably grazed. The line A-A corresponds to the maximum permissible level for large human populations.

It does not yet seem possible to estimate the doses to human tissue due to fall-out, nor their distribution in time, which are necessary data for judging the possible biological significance. Experience during the past year is, however, likely to raise doubts as to the lack of biological importance of the tests of nuclear weapons, at any rate if they are continued on the present scale.

It is extremely difficult to predict what will in the future be the most important sources of radiation caused by artificial radioactive elements distributed in nature. There is reason to believe that the problems of disposal of radioactive wastes will be satisfactorily solved, and that precautions in the handling and use of radioactive material will be adequate, but accidents and unforseen events may gradually spread radioactive substances of medium and long half-life beyond control. These radioactive materials will follow unknown paths, and may be harmful to mankind in ways that will become known to us only after long experience.

REFERENCES

1. Anderson, W., Mayneord, W. V. & Turner, R. C. (1954) *Nature (Lond.)*, **174**, 424
2. Forbes, G. B. & Lewis, A. M. (1956) *J. clin. Invest.*, **35**, 596
3. Great Britain, Medical Research Council (1956) *The hazards to man of nuclear and allied radiations*, London
4. Halliday, D. (1950) *Introductory nuclear physics*, New York, p. 461
5. Hultqvist, B. (1956) *K. svenska VetenskAkad. Handl.*, Ser. 4, **6**, No. 3

6. Hursh, J. B. & Gates, A. (1950) *Nucleonics*, **7**, 46
7. Schaefer, H. J. (1950) *Aviation Med.*, October, p. 383
8. Shohl, A. T. (1939) *Mineral metabolism*, New York, p. 19
9. Sievert, R. M. & Hultqvist, B. (1956) *Brit. J. Radiol.*, Suppl. 7, p. 1
10. Spiers, F. W. (1956) *Appendix J: The dose of radiation received in human tissues from natural sources.* In: Great Britain, Medical Research Council, *The hazards to man of nuclear and allied radiations*, London, p. 107
11. United States of America, National Academy of Sciences (1956) *The biological effects of atomic radiation: summary reports*, Washington, D.C.

DETECTION OF INDUCED MUTATIONS
IN OFFSPRING OF IRRADIATED PARENTS

J. LEJEUNE

*Chargé de Recherche au Centre National de la Recherche scientifique,
Paris, France*

The Problem of the Gonad Dose

Among the various sources of ionizing radiation, apparatus for radiodiagnosis and radiotherapy today represent the main contribution of man to the increase in background radiation.

Radiodiagnosis, which is being carried out more and more frequently every year in all developed countries, at present plays a dominant role in this connexion. Ranging as it does from the radiographs and radioscopies called for by some pathological condition, to the periodic radiographs of the whole skeleton used in studying the growth of normal children, the field of exploratory radiology now covers an extremely large proportion of the population; for example, in France, all children of school age are submitted yearly to systematic radiographic examination.

While there can be no doubt that most radiodiagnostic examinations affect the gonads only very slightly, all examinations of this type which involve the pelvic region may have genetic effects (for example, gynaeco-logical and obstetrical examinations).

One has only to consult the appropriate tables, such as the one drawn up by Plough,[7] to see that radioscopy may involve very high doses: for example, 10 to 20 r per minute for a gastro-intestinal radioscopy. And techniques such as radiocinematography, which, happily, are not used very extensively, are much more harmful, since they involve even higher doses. Several authors have attempted to calculate the mean gonad dose, on the basis of isodose curves, for whole populations. The estimates vary according to the author, but, in general, the gonad dose may be taken as being of the order of one roentgen; in other words, it represents a very considerable fraction of the quantity of natural radiation to which we are inevitably exposed.

Be this as it may, these estimates are based on the assumption that the radiation emitted by such apparatus is of known quality and that the methods employed in its application are standardized, which is very far from being the case. In fact, considering that radioscopic apparatus, often poorly shielded, is to be found more and more frequently in the consulting-rooms of general practitioners, one is justified in concluding that a very high proportion of radioscopic examinations are being carried out by physicians with no formal training in radiology.

In the opinion of the writer and his colleague, Professor R. Turpin, it would be desirable to obtain, by means of surveys among general practitioners as well as in hospitals, an experimental estimate of the gonad dose involved in any given radiological examination, under the actual conditions in which the said examination is carried out. Such surveys would make it possible to check the validity of the extrapolations at present in use.

A simple method would be to place micro-counters—or, perhaps even better, small films of the type used in atomic plants—in contact with the genital organs of all persons examined.

Even if such surveys were to result only in an increase in the precautions taken by those using X-ray apparatus, they would have partially fulfilled their purpose.

Radiotherapy certainly represents a much smaller risk from the genetic point of view, on the one hand because it is carried out by specialists, and on the other because in most cases the people concerned are elderly. Nevertheless, on examining the statistics of the radiotherapeutic services of the Paris hospitals, Turpin, Lejeune & Rethore [9] found that among 238 800 case-histories there were 4428 cases of pelvic irradiation of adults under 35 years of age. The proportion of the total—about 2%—is, of course, low, but it does represent cases in which the radiation has impinged directly on the gonads of subjects who are still young enough to reproduce.

Although the calculation of the gonad dose is much more reliable in radiotherapy than in radiodiagnosis, direct determination during all forms of treatment (even extra-pelvic), by means of films or micro-counters placed in contact with the scrotum or in the vaginal fornix, would also be very desirable.

It follows from the foregoing considerations that the accuracy of an estimate of the mean gonad dose received in 30 years by nubile subjects should be checked by random sampling to determine the dose actually received under various examination conditions. It should be noted, however, that such work will be useless if it is not accompanied by systematic recording of the doses received by every individual in the population.

One method of obtaining systematic records, though perhaps a little startling, has already proved its worth. It entails treating the administration of X-rays in the same way as that of morphine for example, by providing all owners of X-ray apparatus with a counterfoil book (of the type used for prescribing narcotics), in which every radiological operation should be recorded and the following particulars given: name, age and address of patient; reason for the examination; area examined; and details required for calculation of the dose (e.g., kilovolts, milliamperes, type of filter, dimensions of beam, etc.).

In practice, this form of registration would probably involve very considerable difficulties, but the increasing socialization of medicine would probably make it feasible for a known fraction of all radiological operations and would certainly draw the attention of the medical profession to a danger of which it is but little aware at the present time.

Methods for Detection of Mutations Induced in Offspring of Irradiated Subjects

Since human geneticists cannot employ methods such as those used for *Drosophila*, they have to resort to statistical comparison of two populations of children supposedly identical in all respects save the dose of roentgens received by the gonads of their parents.

(*a*) *The study of abnormalities and malformations* may reveal an increase in frequency in the progeny of the irradiated group. This increase could be considered to be linked with the appearance of unfavourable dominant mutations. Although probably reliable in the case of definite genetic syndromes such as achondroplasia, this method is much less precise in respect of congenital abnormalities as a whole, since the latter are affected by extremely varied factors (age of mother, parity, etc.). However, if sufficient data are to be obtained to make it possible to draw conclusions, all abnormalities must be considered.

(*b*) *The study of the frequency of sex-linked recessive diseases* in the sons of irradiated mothers, although theoretically possible, necessitates such a large number of observations that it has not been undertaken.

(*c*) *The production of lethal genes* can be more easily detected. The most serious effect, sterility, is the one most generally known; but measurement of sterility or even of subfertility in man is extremely difficult. As has been remarked elsewhere (Turpin & Lejeune [8]), the actual fertility of civilized populations is hardly a third of the potential fertility of non-Malthusian societies, which greatly diminishes the possibility of demonstrating the effects of sterility.

On the other hand, it is logical to expect the production of dominant lethals to bring about an increase in the frequency of miscarriages, which is difficult to establish, and of stillbirths, which can be obtained with much greater accuracy.

It is, however, essentially in the X-chromosome that the lethal genes can be detected, through a study of the sex ratio. Owing to the chromosomal structure of sex, the X-linked lethal mutations appear in different forms according to the sex of the irradiated parent. Thus, in the offspring of a woman exposed to radiation, dominant lethal mutations linked to the sex chromosome have no effect on the sex ratio, whereas sex-linked recessives bring about a deficit of boys.   The contrary is true of men, in whose progeny only the dominant lethals manifest themselves by bringing about a deficit of girls.

If we call "n" the average number of dominant lethals linked to the X-chromosome in the offspring of men who have received a given dose of roentgens, then the following simple equation should apply:

$$\text{frequency of surviving daughters} = \frac{\text{number observed}}{\text{number expected}} = e^{-n}$$

since the number of mutable loci in the X-chromosome should be large enough for the distribution to be of the Poisson type.   Moreover, since it may be taken as a first approximation that this average number, n, should be identical for all the chromosomes, the autosomally viable zygotes represent a fraction of the total fertilized ova roughly equal to $(e^{-n})^{22}$, and it is in this fraction alone that it will be possible to observe a disturbance of the sex ratio.

Similar reasoning can be applied to the case of the offspring of irradiated women, bearing in mind the fact that there is a relationship between the frequency of the dominant and the recessive lethals.

Since, in theory, the parameter n bears a direct relationship to the roentgen dose received, and since our estimates of the gonad dose are very approximate, there is probably a fairly strong correlation between the actual fertility of the parents after irradiation and the deviation of the sex ratio observed in their progeny.   In other words, the most pronounced variations in the sex ratio would be shown by the offspring of parents who are almost sterile owing to the irradiation of one of them (for example, couples who have only one child).

It follows from the above that, in the absence of an accurate estimate of the gonad dose, an over-all study of the sex ratio of all children born of an irradiated father or mother may, if it does not take into account the number of siblings born after treatment, result in the masking of the phenomenon by a "dilution effect", caused by the very numerous siblings who are the issue of a parent relatively slightly affected.

Further, the problem of control samples can only be correctly solved by comparing children born before and after treatment of the same irradiated parent and thus eliminating any genetic factor due to the couple itself, as well as the possible influence of sibships of one sex only.

Finally, and bearing in mind the above limitations, it would seem that the sex ratio is the most sensitive touchstone for detecting the production of lethal mutations in the first generation of children born of irradiated parents.

Information Available at Present

Relatively few direct investigations of the influence of irradiation have been carried out and the writer will mention them in succession here, under the headings of the three main characteristics referred to earlier: frequency of abnormalities, frequency of miscarriages and stillbirths, and variations in the sex ratio.

(a) Frequency of abnormalities

Murphy & Goldstein [5] and Maurer [4] have published statistics on the offspring of women treated with X-rays or radium in the pelvic region. Unfortunately, neither of these papers can be considered very satisfactory, owing to the lack of detail concerning the families, on the one hand, and the absence of any controls, on the other.

Two recent papers cast more light on this question. In 1953, Neel et al., [6] on studying the offspring of the survivors of the atomic bombing of Nagasaki and Hiroshima, did not find any increase in the frequency of serious abnormalities. While Macht & Lawrence, [3] on comparing the children of fathers who were radiologists with those whose fathers were medical specialists not exposed to ionization risks, found a significant over-all increase in abnormalities among the progeny of the radiologists. Unfortunately, the latter authors on the one hand included as abnormalities syndromes of a very varied and sometimes quite unsuitable nature (foetal erythroblastosis, for example), and on the other accepted the diagnosis made by the parents themselves, who, though admittedly physicians, clearly lacked the necessary objectivity. These considerations greatly limit the significance of the conclusions drawn by Macht & Lawrence, but it is only fair to stress that if, from the authors' data, those relating only to congenital forms of heart disease are selected, the increase pointed out among the progeny of the radiologists remains statistically significant.

(b) Frequency of miscarriages and stillbirths

Macht & Lawrence [3] mention a non-significant increase in the over-all frequency of stillbirths plus miscarriages, while Neel et al. [6] report a non-significant increase in the frequency of stillbirths. Finally, Crow, [1] who studied the offspring of American radiologists through a survey, by questionnaire, which was carried out along lines similar to those followed by Macht & Lawrence, has also reported a slight and non-significant increase in foetal mortality among the progeny of irradiated fathers.

All in all, although the published data agree fairly well on this point, they cannot strictly be regarded as conclusive.

(c)   Variations in the sex ratio

Of the publications already mentioned, only that of Neel et al.[6] supplies any usable material. For example, neither Murphy & Goldstein,[5] nor Maurer[4] nor Crow[1] indicate the sex of the children; and although Macht & Lawrence[3] give some figures, they do not specify the sex of about 10% of the children, so that one can hardly rely on their statistics.

In their preliminary report, Neel et al.[6] showed that among the offspring of the survivors in Nagasaki there was a statistically significant deviation of the sex ratio, an increase being observed among the children of irradiated fathers and a decrease among those of irradiated mothers. On the other hand, such variations were small or non-existent in the more numerous offspring of the Hiroshima survivors.

At the First International Congress of Human Genetics, held in Copenhagen in August 1956, Dr J. V. Neel presented some further statistics on the subjects mentioned above, including all the births which had occurred in these families since 1953. In this larger sample, the deviations observed in 1953 are no longer discernible.

In Paris, a survey has been carried out on the offspring of subjects given pelvic radiotherapy in all the hospitals in the city and the surrounding districts (Turpin, Lejeune & Rethore[9]). The initial findings, which are concerned exclusively with the sex ratio, were presented by Professor Turpin at the First International Congress of Human Genetics; they are briefly summarized in the table on the page opposite.

The figures given in the table show that, before treatment, the sex ratio of the children was statistically comparable in the two groups, i.e., the male and female subjects. After treatment of one of the parents, however, the sex ratio increased in the offspring of the treated fathers and decreased in those of the treated mothers, this heterogeneity being statistically significant.

Conclusions

In concluding this very rapid review of the few usable data at present available, the writer would like to stress the following two points:

1. The gonad dose per 30 years, in the form in which it has already been established,[2,10] probably gives an acceptable approximation of the risk resulting from artificial ionizing radiation. Nevertheless, an accurate evaluation can be arrived at only by systematic recording of all individual exposures. Moreover, it is essential that the gonad dose actually received during irradiation under the conditions obtaining in practice should be checked experimentally. The first—and perhaps the most valuable—result of such investigations would probably be a substantial decrease in the degree of exposure of the gonads.

OFFSPRING OF VARIOUS SUBJECTS BEFORE AND AFTER PELVIC RADIOTHERAPY

	Subjects and reason for treatment	Number of children		Sex ratio
		male	female	
Before treatment	Men (138); various reasons	116	115	0.502 ± 0.034
	Men (284); sciatica	242	223	0.520 ± 0.024
	Women (154)	131	106	0.553 ± 0.034
After treatment	Men (95); various reasons ($\bar{r}^* = 1461$ r)	68	62	0.523 ± 0.048
	Men (194); sciatica ($\bar{r} = 1295$ r)	157	118	0.571 ± 0.030
	Women (97) ($\bar{r} = 1360$ r)	63	73	0.463 ± 0.044

* $\bar{r}$ = average skin dose, *not* gonad dose

2. From an analysis of the observations already made, it appears that with the doses used in radiotherapy, it would probably be possible to detect some effect in the first generation. The urgency of research in this connexion need hardly be stressed. It is only when a list of the mutations which are at present detectable has been drawn up that it will be possible to extrapolate and obtain an estimate of the over-all genetic damage.

REFERENCES

1. Crow, J. F. (1955) *Amer. J. Roentgenol.*, **73**, 467
2. Great Britain, Medical Research Council (1956) *The hazards to man of nuclear and allied radiations*, London
3. Macht, S. H. & Lawrence, P. S. (1955) *Amer. J. Roentgenol.*, **73**, 442
4. Maurer (1933) *Zbl. Gynäk.*, p. 819
5. Murphy, D. P. & Goldstein, L. (1929) *Amer. J. Roentgenol.*, **22**, 207
6. Neel, J. V. et al. (1953) *Science*, **118**, 537
7. Plough (1952) *Nucleonics*, **10**, 17

8. Turpin, R. & Lejeune, J. (1955) *Bull. Acad. nat. Méd. (Paris)*, No 5/6, p. 104
9. Turpin, R., Lejeune, J. & Rethore, M. O. (1956) *Etude de la descendance de sujets traités par radiothérapie pelvienne. Note préliminaire* (Paper presented at the First International Congress of Human Genetics, Copenhagen; unpublished)
10. United States of America, National Academy of Sciences (1956) *The biological effects of atomic radiation*, Washington, D.C.

GONAD DOSES FROM DIAGNOSTIC
AND THERAPEUTIC RADIOLOGY

W. M. COURT BROWN

*Director, MRC Group for Research into the General Effects of Radiation,
Radiotherapy Department, Western General Hospital,
Edinburgh, Scotland*

Diagnostic Radiology

Several estimates have been made recently of the gonad dose to the population, in excess of that from natural background radiation, resulting from diagnostic radiology. These range in value from approximately 10% of the background radiation (Martin [3]) to approximately 58% (Clark [1]). Intermediate between these two is the estimate of Osborn & Smith [4] of at least 22%. There appears to be some agreement, on present knowledge, that the "doubling dose" for man may lie between 30 and 80 r in a period of 30 years. The concept of the "doubling dose" is, however, an over-simplification of the situation, as there most likely exists a spectrum of gene sensitivity. It may well be that already we are in the position that the mutation rate for some genes is significantly raised.

The most comprehensive analysis yet made of the gonad dose from diagnostic radiology is that of Osborn & Smith. [4] These authors make a number of points of importance. First, they draw attention to the rapid expansion in the use of diagnostic X-ray procedures, adducing evidence that in England and Wales the number of X-ray examinations may, at the present time, be increasing by about 12% per year, and that in 1954 between 17 and 18 million examinations were made. They point out, however, that the adverse effect of this expansion, so far as the gonad dose is concerned, is offset to some extent by technical advances which have reduced the amount of necessary radiation exposure. Secondly, Osborn & Smith draw attention to the important fact that only a small number of examinations, amounting to about 7% of the total, contribute the major portion (about 75%) of the gonad dose. These examinations are those of the hips, the lumbo-sacral spine, the pelvis, the urinary tract (intravenous and retrograde pyelography) and pelvimetry. By and large these findings are comparable to those of Martin. [3]

Of serious import is the widespread use of pelvimetry and other X-ray obstetrical examinations of the abdomen, not to speak of examination of the maternal abdomen for other than obstetrical purposes. According to Osborn & Smith, *at least* 26 000 pelvimetries are carried out annually in

England and Wales and 86 000 other obstetrical X-ray examinations. The authors calculate that the maternal gonad dose from pelvimetry alone amounts to 3% of the gonad dose to the total population of both sexes, and the foetal dose to as much as 15.6%.

The real criticism of the work of Osborn & Smith lies in the fact that their results are based on a sample of only five hospitals—two teaching and two non-teaching hospitals and one children's hospital. It is doubtful whether this is an adequately representative sample of the hospitals of England and Wales, particularly as there is some evidence, especially from a study of pelvimetry, of considerable variations in radiographic techniques.

Therapeutic Radiology

The great majority of patients treated in radiotherapy centres are suffering from malignant disease and are either actually or effectively past the reproductive age. However, a proportion of young persons are treated for a variety of non-malignant conditions. These conditions are grouped into those treated during childhood and those treated during early adult life. In the former group are haemangiomata, keloids, hypertrophic tonsillar tissue, bone cysts, etc. The conditions treated during early adult life are mainly ankylosing spondylitis, skin diseases, keloids, some menstrual disturbances and, occasionally, bone cysts.

The childhood conditions chiefly occur on the upper half of the trunk and on the limbs, and, on the whole, are treated with low-voltage radiation given on small localized fields. It is unlikely that these treatments contribute to the gonad dose to any great extent.

Of the conditions irradiated in early adult life, so far as experience in Great Britain is concerned, the treatment of ankylosing spondylitis is likely to contribute an appreciable fraction to the gonad dose. Some tentative estimates which have been made of the size of this fraction are given below. No information is available on the contribution from the treatment of skin diseases, but there is every reason for believing that it may also be appreciable.

Ankylosing Spondylitis

During the past year an epidemiological survey has been carried out to determine the incidence of leukaemia among patients treated with X-rays for ankylosing spondylitis. This survey covered all the radiotherapy departments of England and Wales, and of Scotland, at present operating under the respective National Health Services. In the course of the survey, data were recorded concerning 13 352 patients who were treated between the years 1935 and 1954, inclusive—presumably the majority, if not the great majority, of the patients treated for this disease in Great Britain during the period in question.

It is possible to make some rough and very preliminary estimates of the minimum contribution to the gonad dose as the result of the treatment of ankylosing spondylitis in Great Britain, on the assumption that the testes are not shielded during treatment.

The beneficial effects of X-ray treatment for this disease were only widely recognized during the Second World War, and there was a steady annual increase in the number of new patients irradiated up to 1950, since when there has been a tendency for the number to diminish slightly.   For the period 1949 to 1954 the average number of new cases per year was 1336, of which 1109 (83%) were males.   Of these, 53% were under the age of 35.   Of the females, 43% were less than 35 years of age.

The average standard first course of treatment for a male patient has been taken as follows (based on dosage information from a random sample of approximately one in six of the whole population):

(a)   A single 15 cm × 10 cm posterior field centred over the sacro-iliac joints, the large axis of the field being horizontal.

(b)   A series of fields irradiating the whole length of the spine and extending from the upper margin of the sacro-iliac field to the upper part of the neck.   On an average, the breadth of these fields is 7.5 cm.

(c)   A total skin dose to each field of 1500 r (half value layer, 1.6 mm).

From measurements made in a phantom man it appears that a dose of about 45 r is received in the male gonads during such a course of treatment.

Measurements have not been made of the gonad dose received by females. In some centres the female sacro-iliac area was treated similarly to the male area;   but in many others definite attempts were made to avoid the ovaries.   The direct irradiation of the sacro-iliac region to 1500 r is almost certain to induce permanent sterility.   For present purposes it is assumed that the ovarian dose received is on an average 45 r.

The contributions to the gonad doses every year from the treatment of ankylosing spondylitis have been calculated (see table below) on the basis of the following *de facto* populations for England, Wales and Scotland (1952):

	15-34 years	*All ages*
Males	6.6×10^6	2.37×10^7
Females	6.8×10^6	2.56×10^7
Total	1.34×10^7	4.93×10^7

GONAD DOSE (IN MILLIROENTGENS) PER HEAD OF POPULATION PER YEAR IN ENGLAND, WALES AND SCOTLAND

	15-34 years	*All ages*
Males	4.0	2.1
Females	0.6	0.4
Both sexes	2.3	1.2

These estimates can be considered to be minimal ones. No less than 46% of the males and 44% of the females were given more than one course of treatment. Many of these additional courses were given to the lumbo-sacral region and to the hip joints. However, two other factors, which tend to diminish either the size or the effectiveness of the gonad dose, must be taken into consideration. First, in some radiotherapy centres it was standard practice to provide some form of lead shielding for the testes; this was by no means a universal habit, however, and a number of instances of male infertility, some of which could have been the result of X-ray exposure, were discovered. Secondly, it may well be that sufferers from spondylitis are subfertile. The disease is a crippling one and is frequently accompanied by pulmonary tuberculosis and ulcerative colitis. There is, however, no published evidence on this point.

To sum up, the radiotherapy of patients suffering from ankylosing spondylitis in Great Britain will give a gonad dose per year of at least 1% of the natural background, and possibly appreciably higher. A more rigorous examination of the contribution from this source, and an analysis of the contribution from other types of radiotherapy, including the use of radioactive isotopes, could well bring the total contribution from radio-therapy up to the level of about 8% suggested by Clark[1] for the USA, or perhaps to an even higher level.

Discussion

So far as the writer is aware there is no direct evidence of a steady upward trend in the incidence of any of the undesirable traits that might be expected with any increase in the mutation rate due to the steady expansion of medical radiology. The direct epidemiological approach to this problem is clearly beset with difficulties, not the least being the very large population that would have to be kept under observation and the inaccuracy and inadequacy of death certification.

There is, however, some evidence from which it could be argued indirectly that an increase in undesirable traits may already be taking place. For example, recent work has demonstrated a significant increase in the mortality from leukaemia among persons treated with X-rays for ankylosing spondylitis, and it has also been possible to demonstrate the existence of a relationship between the annual incidence of leukaemia in these patients and the radiation dose to the bone-marrow. Some preliminary data have been published (Court Brown & Doll[2]). On the evidence as it stands it seems possible that radiation leukaemogenesis in man is a non-threshold effect, and that over the range of dose met with in ordinary civilian life the dose-response relationship is a simple proportional one, analogous to that for the induction of mutations. If this were finally shown to be the case, two deductions would become valid. First, that a proportion of naturally occurring cases of leukaemia are probably due to natural background radiation; and, secondly, that any increase in the background radiation from artificial sources will be associated with an increased mortality from leukaemia.

The mortality from leukaemia is known to be rising. Thus, the annual crude death-rate for both sexes rose in England and Wales from 26 in 1940 to 49 in 1954. The corresponding figures for Denmark are 48 and 71, for Canada 30 and 51, and for the USA 39 and 65. Undoubtedly, part of this increase is due to changes in diagnostic criteria and improvements in diagnostic techniques. There is, however, a general feeling that it may in part be real and absolute. If this be the case, and if the dose-response relationship over the relevant range of dose be linear, then part of the increased mortality from leukaemia may well be due to the expanding use of radiations, particularly diagnostic radiology. If the incidence of such traits as haemophilia, muscular dystrophy, and achondroplasia could be examined in the same way, it is possible that at least a qualitatively similar upward trend would be found.

REFERENCES

1. Clark, S. H. (1956) *Bull. atom. Scient.*, **12**, 14
2. Court Brown, W. M. & Doll, R. (1956) *Appendix B: Leukaemia and aplastic anaemia in patients treated with X-rays for ankylosing spondylitis.* In: Great Britain, Medical Research Council, *The hazards to man of nuclear and allied radiations;* London, p. 87
3. Martin, J. H. (1955) *Med. J. Aust.*, **2**, 806
4. Osborn, S. B. & Smith, E. E. (1956) *Lancet*, **1**, 949

MUTATION IN MAN *

L. S. PENROSE

Galton Professor of Eugenics,
University College,
London, England

The study of gene mutation in man has two aspects. The first concerns the ascertainment of spontaneous mutation rates at specified loci. This gives information about human evolution in general as well as about the causation of certain rare diseases and defects. The second aspect, which has only recently become significant, concerns artificially produced mutagens and, in particular, the genetic effects of ionizing radiation. In order to estimate the magnitude of these effects a knowledge of spontaneous mutation rates at given loci is required and the sensitivity of these loci to radiation needs to be ascertained.

Measurement of Spontaneous Mutation Rate

Estimation of mutation rate in man, in relation to any given hereditary trait, depends upon ascertaining three things—the incidence of the trait in the general population, the nature of the genetical contribution to the cause of the trait, and the fitness of the genotypes concerned. These phenomena are not necessarily constant. As seen in the population at the present time they may not represent the true picture over a long series of generations, during which natural selection has been acting. They give us only the first clue to conditions which govern genic equilibrium in human populations.

There are two standard methods of approach, the direct and the indirect.

Direct observation

The most favourable case for estimating mutation rate directly occurs when the gene studied is detectable with certainty or regularity in heterozygotes. Instances of fresh mutation can then be observed in families where a gene appears in an offspring although it was not present in the parents. The ideal kind of regular dominance required for this is rarely (perhaps never) found in human genetics. Man is a wild species,

---

* This paper has also been published in the *Proceedings of the First International Congress of Human Genetics* (see *Acta genet. (Basel),* 1956, 6, 169)

under natural selection, unlike laboratory stocks, and consequently most single gene effects, especially those shown in heterozygotes, are subject to modification. Even with the most reliable characters, such as blood-group antigens, suppression is possible by gene interaction (Levine et al. [20]); such events could easily be misinterpreted by the unwary as evidence of mutation.

The situation for sex-linked genes is quite favourable, theoretically, for direct observation of fresh mutation, because modification of a character shown in hemizygous males is usually slight. Occasional families will be observed in which the probability is very great that the disease in the propositus is due to fresh mutation. The proportion of mutant cases can also be inferred if the sibships show an excess of sporadic propositi.

For recessive traits the problem is much more difficult, because heterozygous carriers are not detectable in ordinary circumstances. In cases where special techniques have been developed for identification of carriers the problem is resolved into one of detection of mutation for a dominant condition, as demonstrated by Vanderpitte et al. [40] for the sickle-cell trait. Direct observation of cases of recessive diseases due to fresh mutation is very unlikely to be possible, because only a very small proportion of cases of a recessive trait in a given generation can be attributed to fresh mutation in a parent. For diseases in which a single gene is only a part cause and in which environment has a great effect upon manifestation, the contribution of spontaneous mutation is likely to be even less significant. The same applies to conditions due to the interaction of many genes. For none of them can mutation rates be directly determined.

The indirect approach

When the total effects of a gene are very disadvantageous, an indirect line of argument can be used for estimating mutation rate, even though the gene may not be manifest in the heterozygous state. Principles on which the indirect estimation of mutation rates can be based were laid down by Haldane. [13] The assumption can be made that the human population is in a state approaching genetical equilibrium under natural selection. It is supposed that disadvantageous genes could not persist in the population unless their extinction by selective mortality were completely balanced by the recurrence of mutation.

In the case of dominant or sex-linked characters associated with very high mortality, the direct measurement of mutation rate can be supplemented, and its plausibility greatly strengthened, by the indirect argument. The best situation for this combination occurs in the case of a very deleterious dominant trait. This is a rare circumstance. If the disease is not very lethal, there will be difficulty in measuring the unfitness conferred by the gene; if it is very lethal, there will be difficulty in proving the dominant mode of inheritance, as it will seldom last even for two gene-rations. Sometimes the problem might be solved for a locus which had seve-ral different known alleles, some producing milder and others severer types of disease. Then, in each of the severest cases, mutation of a lethal allele will be observable. This possibly occurs in both epiloia and chondrodys-trophy. For mild alleles, which last for several generations, the proportion of cases due to fresh mutation is correspondingly smaller.

Estimates which are entirely indirect are untrustworthy, but they have actually been made for a variety of genes recognized only by their recessive effects. One cause of uncertainty with recessive traits is that allowance has to be made for the results of inbreeding. Another likely source of error is that genetical equilibrium can be maintained not only by mutation but also by slightly advantageous effects in heterozygotes. That is to say, on balance, the total effect of a gene may be much less bad than appears from studying abnormal homozygotes, in which case an indirect estimate of mutation rate will give much too high a value.

Some Standard Estimates of Human Mutation Rates

Mutation rates have been calculated for quite a large number of genes in man. It is preferable to express them in terms of loci per generation, if we wish to avoid controversy, because slightly different forms of the diseases concerned can be accounted for by the same allele or by different alleles. If there are several very closely linked loci giving rise to a pseudo-allelic system, the real mutation rate for each separate element is lowered by a factor depending upon the number of elements in the complex.

Dominants

The most exact estimates for supposedly single loci are probably those for very deleterious dominant traits (see Table I). Allowing for the probability that more than one disease entity may be classified under each heading, they are maximal values. The average value for six conditions is about 14×10^{-6}.

Owing to the classification of more than one type of chondrodystrophy under the same heading, the rate given is likely to be considerably too high. According to Grebe[10] there are several clinical types; and some cases may be due to recessive genes. Furthermore, these different types may have different mutation rates.

Another dominant condition which apparently has a relatively high mutation rate, namely, retinoblastoma, occurs perhaps not infrequently as a phenocopy (Vogel[41]), not transmissible to the next generation. The same idea could be applied also to other conditions listed in Table I, such as microphthalmos.

TABLE I. ESTIMATES OF SPONTANEOUS MUTATION RATES OF SOME HUMAN GENES*

Trait	Mutation rate per million loci per generation	Region	Source
Dominant inheritance			
Epiloia	8	England	Gunther & Penrose[12]
Chondrodystrophy	45	Denmark	Mørch [23]
,,	70	Sweden	Böök [2]
Aniridia	5**	Denmark	Møllenbach [22]
Microphthalmos (without mental defect)	5	Sweden	Sjögren & Larsson[37]
Retinoblastoma	15	England	Philip & Sorsby
,, ...	23	USA	Neel & Falls [25]
,, ...	4	Germany	Vogel [41]
Partial albinism and deafness	4	Netherlands	Waardenburg [43]
Sex-linked inheritance			
Haemophilia	20	England	Haldane [14]
,, ...	32	Denmark	Andreassen [1]
,, ...	27	Switzerland and Denmark	Vogel [42]
Pseudohypertrophic muscular dystrophy .	95	USA	Stephens & Tyler [38]
,, . .	45	Northern Ireland	Stevenson [39]
,, . .	43	England	Walton [44]

* After Penrose [31]
** This estimate differs by a factor of 2 from that given by the author, but it is based on his material.
† Based on data of Griffith and Sorsby [11]

The indirect argument, which supports all these estimations, can be used only when there is a strong selection against the gene studied. Theoretically it should be possible to obtain mutation figures for several blood antigens, e.g., ABO or MNS, but selection against any of these genes is too slight and indefinite to be used as indirect support for the mutation hypothesis. On the other hand, the indirect argument can be extended to cover certain cases in which the combination of several genes at different loci is lethal or very deleterious. Thus a lethal condition, caused by the simultaneous presence of two heterozygous genes, will imply that each of the genes concerned mutates frequently enough to make good the loss occasioned when it occurs in conjunction with the other.

Taking all these considerations together we can reasonably assume that the mutation rates for loci giving rise to dominant genes, though somewhat too high, are of the right order of magnitude. It seems that, for most of these dominant diseases, the rate should be considered to be about 5×10^{-6}.

Sex-linked loci

The prevalence in man of sex-linked diseases which are very lethal is difficult to explain except on a mutation hypothesis. Direct evidence, based upon the observed low incidence of haemophilia in sibships and in maternal collateral relatives, also supports this explanation. The matter has been repeatedly investigated by Haldane [16,17] and there seems to be some evidence that mutation more commonly occurs in males than in females. The two sex-linked diseases which have given information about human mutation rates are haemophilia and pseudohypertrophic muscular dystrophy. In both cases there are many types of illness easily confused with one another clinically. Sex-linked types are identified by pedigree studies and by their occurrence in males only; but, by this process, some autosomal cases may occasionally be incorrectly included. A characteristic difficulty is the exclusion of autosomal sex-limited conditions.

In the standard examples of haemophilia and sex-linked muscular dystrophy, mutation rates have been estimated several times, but always on the assumption that, in each disease, there is only one locus involved. These rates, as shown in Table I, are considerably higher than the direct estimates for autosomal dominants. Perhaps the X-chromosome is peculiar in that it has many complex loci or distinct loci with similar effects.

Recessive traits

A recessive trait in man can be defined as one which depends upon a gene in homozygous form. There may be mild manifestations detectable in heterozygotes (e.g., thalassaemia, galactosaemia, cystinuria), but the

TABLE II. INDIRECT ESTIMATES OF SPONTANEOUS MUTATION RATES ON THE ASSUMPTION
OF RECESSIVE INHERITANCE

Trait	Mutation rate per million loci per generation	Region	Source
Juvenile amaurotic idiocy	38	Sweden	Haldane [15]
Albinism	28	Japan	Neel et al. [27]
Icthyosis congenita . .	11	Japan	Neel et al. [27]
Total colour blindness .	28	Japan	Neel et al. [27]
Infantile amaurotic idiocy	11	Japan	Neel et al. [27]
Amyotonia congenita . .	20	Sweden	Böök [2]
Epidermolysis bullosa .	50	Sweden	Böök [2]
Cystic fibrosis of pancreas	700	USA	Goodman & Reed [8]
Sickle-cell anaemia . .	10 000	USA	Neel [24]
Thalassaemia.	400	USA	Neel [24]
Spastic diplegia	2 000	Sweden	Böök [3]
Microcephaly	49	Japan	Komai et al. [18]
Phenylketonuria	25	England	Penrose [31,32]
Schizophrenia	500	England	Penrose [33]

disease in the homozygote is the effect with which we are concerned. The indirect estimates of mutation rates for recessive diseases, shown in Table II, assume that the heterozygote is neutral in its effect upon fitness. If the heterozygotes were deleterious, as suggested by Böök [3] for schizophrenia, the values would have to be increased. Conversely, if the heterozygotes were slightly favourable, the values would have to be reduced.

A very slight amount of heterozygous advantage is sufficient to keep a rare recessive lethal in stable genic equilibrium in the absence of mutation, so that the calculation of mutation rate is very easily invalidated. This is an extremely important principle and is worthy of detailed consideration.

Most well-known recessive traits cannot easily be supposed to have arrived at their existing levels of gene frequency (e.g., 1/100 for phenylketonuria) by chance or by "drift". The situation for commoner genes is even more striking. For thalassaemia and sickle-cell trait (Neel [24]), cystic fibrosis (Goodman & Reed [8]), spastic diplegia (Böök [3]) and schizophrenia (Penrose [33]), improbably high mutation rates have to be postulated. Indeed the maximum rate for sickle-cell trait, derived from direct observation on heterozygotes, is much lower than that calculated indirectly (Vanderpitte et al. [40]). These common traits could not have easily established themselves unless the heterozygotes had some advantage. The advantages may have been local ones in the distant past—for example, ability to withstand infections, plagues, famines, abnormal climates, and so on.

It is not necessary to postulate any virtue in the heterozygote as such. It could be sufficient if the mutant alleles were favourable at one epoch and unfavourable at another epoch, in different circumstances or at different stages of the same life-cycle. The principle of genetical stability produced by heterozygous advantage, or, more accurately, homozygous disadvantage, is one which has been understood for a long time (Fisher [7]) but has only recently been taken seriously. In human genetics it is exhibited by such a system as may be present in relation to the sickle-cell trait in Africans. The disadvantage of one homozygote, SS, which suffers from anaemia, is balanced to some extent by the disadvantage of the homozygote, AA, which is especially susceptible to malaria caused by *Plasmodium falciparum*. Balanced human genetical systems are shown in metrical traits because the extreme types, which tend to be homozygous, are relatively unfavourable. Examples are stature, birth weight and intelligence level. For intelligence, in particular, there is a marked fertility differential in one direction and a viability differential in the other. That is, low intelligence levels are associated with low viability and high levels with low fertility.

In all such cases of balanced polymorphism the variation, which is apparently reduced in each generation by loss of extreme types, is not maintained by fresh mutation. It is maintained simply because the heterozygotes, who tend to have medium metrical value, are the parents of most children in each successive generation. In these circumstances it is quite useless to attempt to estimate the mutation rates of component genes: any indirect estimate will be far too high.

It has been suggested by Haldane [15] that the converse may be true—namely, that mutation-rate estimates for recessive traits are often too low. The argument used is that the true incidence, which recurrent mutation would theoretically balance, has in the past been much greater than it is at the present time. This is likely because inbreeding, which facilitates the appearance of recessive diseases, has been gradually diminishing for many decades in all civilized communities. The writer believes this argument to be unsound because the incidence of rare recessive traits in man is extremely irregularly distributed. Tay-Sachs disease is almost confined to Jewish communities, as also is pentosuria, while Cooley's disease has its centre in the Po delta. Phenylketonuria, on the other hand, does not occur among Jews. Sickle-cell anaemia is common in Africans. Juvenile amaurotic idiocy is commonest in Sweden and acatalazaemia has been found only in Japan. These facts suggest that recessive mutations are very rare, but that occasionally they have spread for unknown reasons probably connected with heterozygous advantage at one epoch or another. If mutations were not very rare, the same set of recessive diseases would appear in all communities, or at least in all inbred communities, throughout the world.

To sum up the discussion on spontaneous mutation rate, my view is that, for a variety of reasons, most mutation rates already calculated are too high; points to be stressed are, first, that mutation may be mimicked by suppression of even the most regular kinds of dominant inheritance; secondly, that different conditions are grouped under single clinical headings; and, thirdly, that heterozygotes of established recessive lethal traits are likely to have carried slight advantages in the past even if they do not at the present time.

Effect of Induced Mutations

The immediate effect of an increase above spontaneous mutation rate is most easily calculated when the gene is dominant. The rule, however, is quite general. The increase in incidence of any trait in the first generation, due to induced mutation, depends upon the proportion of cases due to fresh mutation in ordinary circumstances. For lethal dominants and sex-linked traits this proportion is large, but in lethal recessives it is very small. It is also small for dominants which are very imperfectly manifested, as it is with those contributing to multifactorial traits. The rule refers to the effect in the first generation or in closely succeeding generations, which especially interest people now living. The total quantitative effect, on the population, of altered mutation rate is theoretically the same whatever the manner of inheritance, but in the case of recessives or heavily modified dominants, a slight effect is maintained over an enormous length of time, many thousands of years.

The proportion of cases of a lethal condition due to fresh mutation in any given generation can be estimated on the basis of the indirect argument. If the mutation rate, μ, is expressed as a function of the gene frequency thus,

$$\mu = f(q)$$

it follows formally that the proportion of cases in any given generation due to fresh mutation, a quantity which can be called M, is given by the approximation,

$$M = d\mu \ / \ dq.$$

For example, for a recessive lethal trait,

$$\mu = q^2, \text{ and so } M = 2q.$$

Substituting 1/40 000 for q^2, the frequency of juvenile amaurotic idiocy as estimated by Sjögren, [36] we get $M = 1/100$. In view of what has been said about the use of the indirect method, this is probably an upper limit; but it shows what little effect a change in spontaneous mutation rate would have upon the incidence in the next generation after it had occurred or, indeed, in any subsequent generation. Doubling the mutation rate would only increase the incidence by 1 % in the first subsequent generation.

Sensitivity of Human Loci to Radiation

Much has been written about the probable sensitivity of human loci to radiation, using experimental data on lower animals as a basis for comparison. Direct observations on man, however, are essential, and three sources of information are at present available.

Comparison of offspring of selected parents exposed to different quantities of radiation

This is the method attempted in several comparative studies. Children of radiologists have been examined by Crow [6] and also by Macht & Lawrence, [21] and the exposed Japanese population has been investigated by Neel and his colleagues (Neel & Schull [26]). A development of the same idea is implied in two other proposed types of investigation. One of these is the special examination of children of patients who have received large therapeutic doses of radiation before conception, as may be the case in sufferers from spondylitis. The other suggested method is to examine the incidence of mutations in areas where the natural background radiation is high. Each of these methods, though theoretically possible, has its own special technical difficulties. Moreover, there is a general objection to all of them. Fresh mutation is a phenomenon which can only very rarely be observed even though it may be occurring all the time. To search for slight increases in the incidence of traits which, in the case of known recessives, will not exceed 1 % requires the collection of enormous quantities of data, and the results are likely to be inconclusive. These methods are, in fact, rather inefficient even after allowances have been made for sources of error peculiar to each type of inquiry.

Examination of parental history in known instances of mutation

An alternative and more efficient method, which has received scant attention hitherto, is the careful examination of the personal histories of parents and, in certain instances, of grandparents, for groups of cases where fresh mutation is suspected of having played a part in causing disease in the offspring. This method has already produced valuable results by using the simple test of parental age.

TABLE III.   MEAN PARENTAL AGES IN SPORADIC CASES OF DISEASES ATTRIBUTED
TO FRESH MUTATION COMPARED WITH CONTROL MEAN AGES

Disease	Source*	Control mean**	Number of cases	Excess over control mean (years)	
				father's mean age	mother's mean age
Chondrodystrophy	Mørch [23]	D	97 ⎫	+5.4 ⎫	+3.5 ⎫
	Krooth [19]	E	16 ⎬ 176	+6.8 ⎬ +5.1	+5.7 ⎬ +3.6
	Grebe [10]	G	63 ⎭	+4.3 ⎭	+3.1 ⎭
Acrocephalo-syndactyly	Grebe [9]	G	7	+5.5	+3.5
Epiloia	Gunther & Penrose [12]	E	12 ⎫	+0.8 ⎫	+0.3 ⎫
	Borberg [4]	D	21 ⎬ 33	+0.4 ⎭ +0.5	+0.5 ⎭ +0.4
Neurofibromatosis	Borberg [4]	D	49	+0.9	+0.8
Retinoblastoma	Neel & Falls [25]	M	64	+0.5	+0.7
Mongolism	Schulz [35]	G	80 ⎫	+5.3 ⎫	+7.7 ⎫
	Øster [28]	D	369 ⎬ 664	+5.3 ⎬ +5.8	+6.5 ⎬ +6.9
	Penrose [30]	E	215 ⎭	+6.8 ⎭	+7.4 ⎭

```
  * See Penrose [34]
 ** E  =  England      :  father 30.9;  mother 28.6
    D  =  Denmark      :    "    33.3;    "    28.6
    G  =  Germany      :    "    32.6;    "    28.9
    M  =  Michigan, USA :    "    30.5;    "    26.4
```

Clearly, the older the parent the more likely he is to have been subjected to mutagenic influences. If the influence is background radiation, at the age of 40 the dose will have been twice that received at the age of 20. The net effect on parental age distribution of diseases in the offspring caused by background radiation alone, though definite, would be slight. The expected average increase would be scarcely more than one year above normal parental age (Penrose [30]) .Marked effects confined to one or other parent, however, have been observed in several malformations. Marked increase of father's age has been found in chondrodystrophy and acrocephalo-syndactyly, as shown in Table III. On the other hand, the incidence of mongolism is associated solely with advancing age of the mother. It would appear, thus, that, in so far as these traits may have their origin in fresh mutations, the causes must be different. In particular, a marked increase in paternal age strongly suggests some process connected with cell division in the spermatogonial stage which might be chemical in origin. The effect does not appear in other traits thought to be often caused by fresh mutation, such as epiloia, neurofibromatosis and retinoblastoma, where only slight and statistically insignificant parental age increases have been registered. Mongolism would, by the same test, appear to have an entirely different cause. The effects are set out graphically in the figure below.

**EXCESS OF PARENTAL AGES OVER POPULATION AVERAGE
IN CONDITIONS THOUGHT TO BE DUE TO FRESH MUTATION**

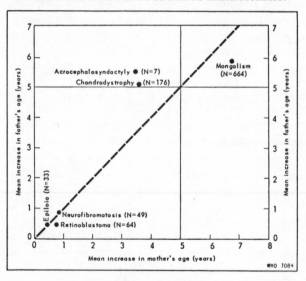

N = *number of observations*

The investigation of parental age is only one part of the problem. The history of parental exposure to X-rays and to other kinds of radiation needs to be recorded; occupational risks and possible exposure to chemical mutagens from external sources could also be made the subject of inquiry.

Observations on somatic cells

It has been suggested that a tissue culture treated by exposure to a known dose of radiation could serve to investigate the sensitivity of human cells. Techniques for this purpose will no doubt be developed in time, though such experiments may never be critical because germ cells could have different sensitivity from that of somatic cells. This objection may for the moment be left on one side, however, while we search for existing data which might give clues to mutation rate in somatic cells. The obvious source of information is observations concerning inductions of tumours by radiation.

It has until recently usually been assumed that very small amounts of ionizing radiation have no effect on the induction of leukaemia. This is now doubted, and the relation between bone-marrow dose and incidence of leukaemia is thought to be not unlike the linear effect observed in the induction of X-chromosome lethals in *Drosophila*. Some idea of the dosage to bone-marrow required to double the spontaneous leukaemia rate can be obtained from the data of Court Brown & Doll,[5] and it is in the region of 30 to 50 r.

This line of thought leads to another interesting idea. The suggestion has been made that many sporadic cases of retinoblastoma arise as phenocopies. Is it not possible that these phenocopies are simply somatic mutations of the same kind as that which is sometimes carried in the germ track, causing a dominant type of inheritance?

The "Load" of Abnormal Genes in Man

Finally, the writer would like to mention one or two points about the total effect of mutation on man, since this has been so much discussed recently. Consider the total number of zygotes formed in a generation. We have no idea how many fail to pass through the first few divisions and never develop into embryos. Indeed, it is impossible to deduce how many embryos are lost in the first six weeks after fertilization. According to Yerushalmy,[45] 15% of human pregnancies are known to terminate in miscarriages or abortions. Beyond this, 3% result in stillbirths and 2% in neonatal deaths. In addition, early mortality after the first month amounts to 3%. These are figures for European and North American communities, where infectious diseases and malnutrition are under efficient control. In many parts of the world they would be gross underestimates. Among those who survive to adult status, 20% are unmarried and of those who do marry some 10% are infertile. How much of this continuous loss of zygotes, which may amount to about 50%, is genetic is not known; by analogy with results obtained on ordinary metrical traits such as stature and intelligence, about half of this loss of zygotes might be directly hereditary.

Perhaps the main factors are recessive lethals.   If this were so, the indirect argument would lead to the conclusion that about a quarter of zygotes are lost each generation and that the genes which are thereby eliminated are replaced by fresh mutations.   This points to the further conclusion that a large increase in mutation rate, say permanent doubling, would eventually increase this lethal lead to a half and would greatly reduce human fitness, though the immediate effects would be small.   However, for reasons given earlier, the writer does not suppose this picture to be an accurate one. Much of the permanent lethality which we experience is likely to be due to balanced genetic mechanisms, which do not require the assumption of appreciable amounts of mutation to maintain them.   As the writer has pointed out previously,[29] improved living conditions are likely to reduce the frequencies of recessive genes whose prevalence is due to heterozygous advantage. Thus, genetic damage which may be done by the increase in mutation rate, due to industrial and medical uses of radiation, may be offset in the future by the improvements in hygiene which are taking place at the present time all over the world.

REFERENCES

1. Andreasson, M. (1943) *Op. dom. Biol. hered. hum. (Kbh.)*, **6**
2. Böök, J. A. (1952) *J. Génét. hum.*, **1**, 24
3. Böök, J. A. (1953) *Acta genet. (Basel)*, **4**, 1
4. Borberg, A. (1951) *Acta psychiat. (Kbh.)*, Suppl. 71, p. 3
5. Court Brown, W. M. & Doll, R. (1956) *Appendix B: Leukaemia and aplastic anaemia in patients treated with X-rays for ankylosing spondylitis*. In: Great Britain, Medical Research Council, *The hazards to man of nuclear and allied radiations*, London, p. 87
6. Crow, J. F. (1955) *Amer. J. Roentgenol.*, **73**, 467
7. Fisher, R. A. (1930) *The genetical theory of natural selection*, Oxford
8. Goodman, H. O. & Reed, S. C. (1952) *Amer. J. hum. Genet.*, **4**, 59
9. Grebe, H. (1944) *Z. menschl. Vererb.- u. KonstitLehre*, **28**, 209
10. Grebe, H. (1955) *Chondrodysplasie*, Roma
11. Griffith, A. D. & Sorsby, A. (1944) *Brit. J. Ophthal.*, **28**, 279
12. Gunther, M. & Penrose, L. S. (1935) *J. Genet.*, **31**, 413
13. Haldane, J. B. S. (1932) *The causes of evolution*, London
14. Haldane, J. B. S. (1935) *J. Genet.*, **31**, 317
15. Haldane, J. B. S. (1939) *Ann. Eugen. (Camb.)*, **2**, 232
16. Haldane, J. B. S. (1947) *Ann. Eugen. (Camb.)*, **13**, 262
17. Haldane, J. B. S. (1956) *Ann. hum. Genet.*, **20**, 344
18. Komai, T., Kishimoto, K. & Osaki, Y. (1955) *Amer. J. hum. Genet.*, **7**, 51
19. Krooth, R. S. (1952) *The aetiology of human malformations*, London (Thesis)
20. Levine, P. et al. (1955) *Blood*, **10**, 1100
21. Macht, S. H. & Lawrence, P. S. (1955) *Amer. J. Roentgenol.*, **73**, 442
22. Møllenbach, C. J. (1947) *Op. dom. Biol. hered. hum. (Kbh.)*, **15**
23. Mørch, E. T. (1941) *Op. dom. Biol. hered. hum. (Kbh.)*, **3**
24. Neel, J. V. (1951) *Cold. Spr. Harb. Symp. quant. Biol.*, **15**, 141
25. Neel, J. V. & Falls, H. F. (1951) *Science*, **114**, 419

26. Neel, J. V. & Schull, W. J. (1954) *Human heredity*, Chicago
27. Neel, J. V. et al. (1949) *Amer. J. hum. Genet.*, 1, 156
28. Øster, J. (1953) *Mongolism*, Copenhagen
29. Penrose, L. S. (1955) *Advanc. Sci.*, 11, 387
30. Penrose, L. S. (1955) *Lancet*, 2, 312
31. Penrose, L. S. (1956) *Appendix C: The spontaneous mutation rate in man*. In: Great Britain, Medical Research Council, *The hazards to man of nuclear and allied radiations*, London, p. 90
32. Penrose, L. S. (1956) *Appendix D: Calculation of the quantitative effects of spontaneous and induced mutation rates in diseases caused by single genes*. In: Great Britain, Medical Research Council, *The hazards to man of nuclear and allied radiations*, London, p. 93
33. Penrose, L. S. (1956) *Appendix E: Estimate of the incidence of cases of schizophrenia and manic depressive reaction due to spontaneous mutation*. In: Great Britain, Medical Research Council, *The hazards to man of nuclear and allied radiations*, London, p. 96
34. Penrose, L. S. (1956) *Modern Problems in Ophthalmology*, 1, 501
35. Schulz, B. (1931) *Z. ges. Neurol. Psychiat.*, 134, 268
36. Sjögren, T. (1931) *Die juvenile amaurotische Idiotie*, Lund
37. Sjögren, T. & Larsson, T. (1949) *Acta psychiat. (Kbh.)*, Suppl. 56, p. 1
38. Stephens, F. E. & Tyler, F. H. (1951) *Amer. J. hum. Genet.*, 3, 111
39. Stevenson, A. C. (1953) *Ann. Eugen. (Camb.)*, 18, 50
40. Vanderpitte, J. M. et al. (1955) *Blood*, 10, 341
41. Vogel, F. (1954) *Z. KonstLehre*, 32, 308
42. Vogel, F. (1955) *Z. ges. Blutforsch.*, 1, 91
43. Waardenburg, P. J. (1951) *Amer. J. hum. Genet.*, 3, 195
44. Walton, J. M. (1955) *Ann. hum. Genet.*, 20, 1
45. Yerushalmy, J. (1945) *Ann. Amer. Acad. pol. Soc. Sci.*, 237, 134

POSSIBLE AREAS WITH SUFFICIENTLY DIFFERENT BACKGROUND-RADIATION LEVELS TO PERMIT DETECTION OF DIFFERENCES IN MUTATION RATES OF "MARKER" GENES

A. R. GOPAL-AYENGAR

Head, Biology Division, Department of Atomic Energy,
Indian Cancer Research Centre, Bombay

The impressive developments in atomic research in recent years and the increasing application of nuclear energy in many fields of human endeavour have brought to the forefront serious problems concerning the long-term effects of radiation on man and his environment. In order to obtain a better appreciation of the totality of effects on human populations, it is necessary first to take into account the magnitude of the various components of natural background radiation as well as the radioactive elements normally present in the body and environment. The magnitude of the contributions of cosmic rays, radioactive radiations from the earth's surface and radioactive elements in the body is shown in Table I.

In his paper (see page 63), Professor R. M. Sievert has dealt with the naturally occurring sources of radiation and measurements of low-level radioactivity. No attempt will therefore be made here to traverse this ground again.

Monazite Areas

In this paper, the writer will endeavour to show that conditions in certain parts of India are particularly favourable for studies of the differences in mutation rates due to differences in background radiation. But before doing so, it may perhaps not be out of place to say a few words about thorium ores and monazite, since it is these constituents on the earth's surface that contribute to the build-up of natural background levels in certain areas.

Like uranium, thorium is a derivative of acid rocks and is for the most part concentrated in granites, syenites and their corresponding pegmatites. There is, however, a basic geochemical difference between the two radioactive elements, in that while the weathering of thorium ores supervenes by and large by a process of physical comminution, that of uranium ores is acted upon by chemical processes. In consequence, thorium becomes

TABLE I. LEVEL OF EXPOSURE OF HUMAN BODY TO BACKGROUND RADIATION,
EXPRESSED IN MILLIROENTGENS PER YEAR*

I. Radioactive elements in the body

Radioactive carbon
(15 disintegrations per minute
per gram of carbon) . . .   2

Radioactive potassium
(1980 disintegrations per
minute per gram of potassium)   19

Radium
(3.7 × 10¹⁰ disintegrations
per second per gram of
radium) . . . .   7 ?

II. Cosmic rays

	Equator	High latitudes
Sea level	33	37
5 000 feet	40	60
10 000 »	80	120
15 000 »	160	240
20 000 »	300	450

III. Radioactive radiations from earth's surface

Granite rock: 90
  abundance in parts per
  million (typical):
   U   Th   K
   4   13   3 × 10⁴

Sedimentary rock: 23
  U, Th and K about one
  quarter as abundant as in
  granite

Ocean: 0
  abundance in parts per
  million:
   U   Th   K
  2 × 10⁻³ 10⁻⁵ 4 × 10²

Uranium (ore content, 0.1% U)
rock:
  flat surface 2800
  inside mine (2 × 2800) . . 5600

Phosphate rock:
(U content, about 0.01-0.025%)
  flat surface . . . . 280 - 700

Total: I + II + III
At Equator (Sea Level)

21 + 33 + 90 = 144

21 + 33 + 23 = 77

21 + 33 + 0 = 54

* Based on data of Libby[2]

incorporated into sediments as discrete, detrital grains of primary mineral, whereas secondary uranium in sedimentary formation occurs as a diffuse, chemically adsorbed entity on carbonaceous matter, phosphates and clays. The usual ore minerals of thorium are monazite, thorite and thorianite. Of these, mention will be made only of monazite, the principal one.

Without entering into any detailed description of the mode of formation of monazite or the manner in which it finds its way into the sea—aspects which legitimately belong to the province of geology—the writer will pass on to the stage where it is found to accumulate as beach-sand deposits in different parts of the world.

As to geographical areas, monazite deposits have been found admixed with ilmenite, rutile, zircon and other rare-earth elements in patches along the coastline of India. The monazite has accumulated along the sea-shores by a process of natural concentration out of the products of rock decay in the course of long geological ages. The heaviest deposits occur in Travancore-Cochin State, in the south-west part of India. Here, over a stretch of about 100 miles (160 km), the coastline is characterized by patches of this radioactive sand. The most concentrated distribution is to be found over a 12-mile range from Neendakara to Kayankulam and in another stretch, a mile long, at Manavala-Kurichi. Although the monazite constitutes only 1% of the beach sand, the thorium content in it is one of the highest in the world, amounting to about 10.5%. Small pockets of the littoral belt also contain even higher amounts (33%).

Other areas of the world worth mentioning in this context are: Brazil, Ceylon, Indonesia, Australia, the Belgian Congo, parts of the USSR, South Africa, Madagascar, Korea, Spain and the USA. According to Davidson,[1] the beach-sand deposits of Brazil are situated in the States of Rio de Janeiro, Espirito Santo, Bahia, Parahíba and Rio Grande do Norte, extending along a coastline of more than 1000 miles, the largest accumulation being at Comaxatiba and Guaratiba in Bahia, Guarapary in Espirito Santo, Barra do Itabopoana in Rio de Janeiro and the so-called "fossil bar". Although the ratio of monazite to the other minerals is higher than in the Indian and most other sands, the Brazilian concentrate apparently has only 5-6% of thoria, as compared with 10% in Travancore.

Measurements

A preliminary sample survey of the monazite areas of Travancore-Cochin was carried out recently by the Health Physics and Air Monitoring Divisions of the Department of Atomic Energy, Government of India, to estimate the internal and external radiation exposures of the population living in the coastal areas. A more extended series of measurements is under way to obtain detailed information on the levels of activity in the areas of highest background radiation, where there is also a high population density. Measurements have also been taken in and around the houses at the active area.

The external radiation exposure in the region is caused by:

(a) β-γ radiation from natural uranium and thorium contained in the monazite, and

(b) β-γ radiation from radon, thoron and their decay products in the air (Table II).

The external exposure to alpha-radiation is not important because of the small range of the particles.

TABLE II. THE THORIUM SERIES

Name	Symbol	Half-life	Energy of radiation (Mev.)		
			α	β	γ
Thorium . .	$_{90}Th^{232}$	1.39×10^{10} years	4.03	—	0.05
Mesothorium 1	$_{88}Ra^{228}$ (MsTh$_1$)	6.7 years	—	0.02	0.03
Mesothorium 2	$_{89}Ac^{228}$ (MsTh$_2$)	6.13 hours	—	2.1, 1.7 1.0	0.06,0.97
Radiothorium.	$_{90}Th^{228}$ (RdTh)	1.90 years	5.42 \ 5.34 /	—	0.084 \ 0.087 /
Thorium X . .	$_{88}Ra^{224}$ (ThX)	3.64 days	5.68 \ 5.45 } 5.19 /	—	0.24 \ 0.05 /
Thoron. . . .	$_{86}Pa^{220}$ (Th)	54.5 seconds	6.28	—	—
Thorium A . .	$_{84}Po^{216}$ (ThA)	0.158 seconds	6.77	—	—
Thorium B . .	$_{82}Pb^{212}$ (ThB)	10.6 hours	—	0.33 \ 0.57 /	0.24,0.30\ 0.11,0.25/
Thorium C . .	$_{83}Bi^{212}$ (ThC)	60.5 minutes	6.05 \ 6.09 /	2.25	0.04 \ 2.2 /
Thorium C'. .	$_{84}Po^{212}$ (ThC')	3×10^{-7} seconds	8.78	—	—
Thorium C''. .	$_{81}Tl^{208}$ (ThC'')	3.1 minutes	—	1.79	2.65,0.58\ 0.51,0.23} 0.86 /
Thorium D . .	$_{82}Pb^{208}$ (ThD)	Stable	—	—	—

Measurements were made with a thin window β-γ, Geiger-Müller counter with a thickness of 20-30 mg/cm². The measuring instrument was calibrated with a thin-walled ionization chamber. Measurements of this nature have also been carried out in Sweden by Professor Sievert who, as we have seen, has been interested mainly in the measurement of low levels of activity, particularly the γ-radiation from living subjects. On the basis of his painstaking studies he has built up what is probably the most complete body of knowledge obtained so far on radiation exposure in human material of all age-groups.

The internal exposure to the population on the monazite sands is caused by the intake of radioactive substances through air, water and food. Moreover, radon and thoron emanating from monazite will add to the contamination of the air in the vicinity. However, these gases decay in the air, and their decay products get attached to fine dust particles in the air from whence they settle down on the soil or on the population. When the air is breathed, a considerable portion of the active dust is retained in the respiratory system, where it undoubtedly acts on the epithelium. The intake of soluble compounds of uranium and thorium through food and water would increase the body burden of uranium and thorium through ingestion and become a permanent source of internal irradiation. The accompanying schematic diagram gives an idea of the disintegration of thorium and its decay products.

DISINTEGRATION OF THORIUM AND ITS DECAY PRODUCTS

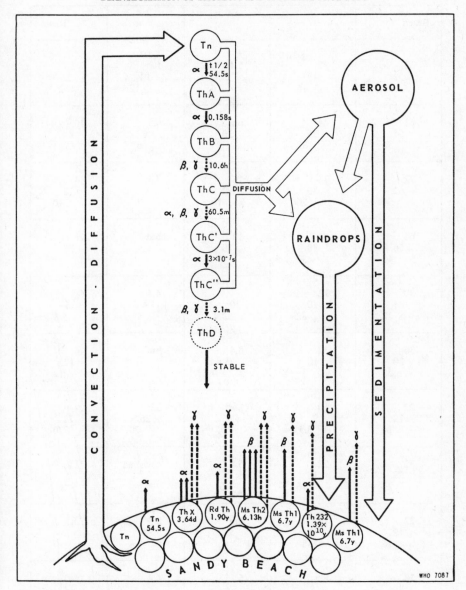

Representative series of measurements taken on the beach, at the surface and in the air, as well as those in the houses, are given in Tables III to VI. These relate to Neendakara-Chavara (Table III), Saktikulankara (Table IV), Pandarathuruthu (Table V) and parts of Midalam (Table VI).

TABLE III. INVESTIGATIONS AT NEENDAKARA-CHAVARA BEACH*

Beach				Road
62 52 48	82 18 16	5.4 5 4.6	14 12 12	2.2 2 2
62 54 50	44 36 32	hut 10 9	6.5 6 6	10 8 7
72 62 56	34 30 26	16 12 10	7.5 7 7	14 12 10
64 56 46	44 38 32	12 10 9	hut .	28 24 20
30 24 22	12 10 8.5	. 10 8.4	4.4 4 3	6.5 6 5.8
36 30 28	12 10 8	8.4 8.4 7.5	hut	16 12 12
22 18 14	10 9 8.5	hut . .	32 26 20	24 22 20
32 28 24	22 18 16	5.4 5 5	cowshed	2.2 2 2
22 18 16	12 10 8	hut . .	8.5 8 7.8	7.8 7.4 7
10 8 7.5	8.5 8 7.5	6 5.6 5.2	4.2 4 3.8	16 14 12

* An area of one mile by about 500 yards was scanned by taking ten points along the length and five across the width.

Reading from left to right, the three figures in each square refer to actual counts of surface $\beta+\gamma$, surface γ, and air γ, respectively.

For $\beta+\gamma$, 100 counts = 10.15 r per year

For γ, 100 counts = 2.86 r per year

TABLE IV.   INVESTIGATIONS AT SAKTIKULANKARA (SOUTH OF NEENDAKARA-
CHAVARA BEACH GRIDLINES) *

100 yards			
56 44 40	36 28 24	18 14 12	14 10 8.6
72 58 50	12 9 7.5	14 10 8 A	12 9 7.4
72 58 48	22 18 14	12 10 8	12 10 8.2
44 36 30 B	20 14 12	72 60 48	12 10 8.4
20 16 14	28 20 16	32 22 18	16 12 10
16 12 10	28 20 16	32 24 20	14 12 10 C
8 7.5 7	32 24 22	22 18 16	22 18 14

(left margin label: 30-50 yards)

* Most of the area scanned is covered with coconut plantations, the coconut pits being filled with the sand from the beach.   Cross-road activity, one furlong from beach, is 7.

Reading from left to right, the three figures in each square refer to actual counts of surface $\beta + \gamma$, surface γ and air γ, respectively.

For $\beta + \gamma$, 100 counts = 10.15 r per year

For γ, 100 counts = 2.86 r per year

A:	hut entrance	8	B:	hut entrance	24	C:	hut entrance	22
	yard (black sand)	30		floor	12		floor	12
	floor	7.5		wall	10		wall	10
	wall	6.4						

It will be seen that there is considerable variation in the intensities of the radiation at different points in the measured areas.   While the actual amount of radiation that the population receives must remain speculative to a certain extent at this stage, the balance of evidence seems to point to the fact that the population is subjected to fairly high doses.   The estimated values in terms of γ doses for different regions range from 200 mr/year to about 2.6 r/year. It is further estimated that the population would be exposed to a total γ dose of about 10-30 r over a reproductive span of 30 years. It may be mentioned in this connexion that Travancore State has the highest density of population in India; the estimated number of inhabitants in the monazite area is of the order of 100 000. It should be stressed here that the total β-γ dose in all cases was 3.5 times higher than that due to γ alone. Although in normal circumstances the β dose could be considered to have a negligible effect, the fact that the decay products of thorium, mesothorium 2 (2.1 Mev.) and thorium C (2.25 Mev.) are high β-energy emitters should not be lost sight of, especially when it is considered that the people come into close contact with the surface of the soil every time they sit or sleep on it. A correction factor would therefore have to be applied to the γ doses in order to estimate the total dose to the whole body as well as to the gonads.

TABLE V.   INVESTIGATIONS AT PANDARATHURUTHU *

Beach				Canal
18 16 14.2	12 9.4 8.8	16 14 12	10.4 9 8.4	8 7.5 7
9.2 8 7.6	16 14 12	9 8.2 7.8	12 10 10	7.6 7 6.4
16 14 12	12 9.6 9	hut	10 8.8 8	7.6 7 6.6
22 18 14	10 8.6 8	14 12 10	9.6 9 8.6	8.4 8 7.6

* An area of 100 yards by 50 yards, one mile down towards Chavara from Cheriaakhiakal, was scanned by taking four points along the beach and five across it.
   Reading from left to right, the three figures in each square refer to actual counts of surface β+γ, surface γ. and air γ, respectively.
   For β+γ, 100 counts = 10.15 r per year
   For γ, 100 counts = 2.86 r per year
   Hut: entrance   10   8.6   8
          floor   10   8.4   8
          wall   8.0

Possibilities of Detecting Differences in Spontaneous Mutation Rates

It has become all too clear that the compilation of exact genetical data on man is beset with numerous difficulties: for one thing, there are no pure strains to work with; for another, the generation times are inordinately long. There is also the probability that many of the radiation-

TABLE VI. INVESTIGATIONS AT MIDALUM (MIDALUM TERI SANDHILL)

Location	Surface		Air
	$\beta + \gamma$	γ	γ
Black sandy patch . . .	18	14	12
Black sandy stream, 1000 yards from the sea, 500 yards from sandhill . .	76	70	60
In centre of six huts . . .	24	22	20
Black and yellow spots on another stream		90	80
,, ,, *	90	80	80
Near-by garden, 100 yards upstream	18	14	12
Inside the hut:			
entrance	9.5	8.8	8
floor	13	12	12
wall	—	12	—
Centre of 20 huts in locality	—	8	7.5
Market	14	12	11.5
In centre of locality on wet ground	—	12	—
Hotel floor.	12	10	9.5

* An underground measurement made here gave a γ count of > 100.

induced genetic changes would be lethal. A considerable number of recessive mutations are passed through successive generations and may express themselves as physiological aberrations that weaken but do not necessarily kill the individual. In such cases, distinction from incidental disease processes may be difficult if not impossible, and may therefore never be resolved. Many mutations induced by radiation may be expected to affect the fertilized ovum, and hence abortions, foetal deaths, stillbirths, infant mortality, malformations, sex ratios, viability and fertility, etc., are the genetic changes most readily seen and analysed statistically. But what we need to look into also are the possibilities of detecting differences in the mutation rates of "marker" genes of populations exposed to radiation of the order present in the monazite area of Travancore. A careful study of the population structure in this area should furnish information concerning gene frequencies and their distribution in time and space, as well as data on mutation rates. Several years ago, Muller [3] raised the question of the possibility that genic erosion will result in a piling up of deleterious mutations following ameliorative medical practices. Now, in the monazite belt of Travancore we have an almost unique situation, where there would appear to be no relaxation of the forces of selection on the population, since the alleviating action of modern medical services has not found its expression to any appreciable degree. The population has been more or less stationary for generations and might be expected to show differences in mutation rates for particular traits — autosomal dominants or sex-linked recessives of the type discussed by Professor A. C. Stevenson in his paper (see page 125). A control population of comparable dimensions, with similar demographic conditions and normal background radiation, exists in the nearby areas.

An inquiry of such a nature would obviously be a long-range one, but would be well worth doing in view of the possibility of thus obtaining some direct evidence on the genetic consequences of naturally occurring high background radiation. The investigation would also be likely to shed light on the dosage relationships for doubling the spontaneous mutation rate and other cognate problems. Moreover, it might also reveal interesting somatic effects, such as the incidence of leukaemia, cancer and other conditions.

REFERENCES

1. Davidson, C. F. (1956) *Mining Mag.*, **94**, 197
2. Libby, W. F. (1955) *Science*, **122**, 58
3. Muller, H. J. (1950) *Amer. J. hum. Genet.*, **2**, 111

COMPARISONS OF MUTATION RATES AT SINGLE LOCI IN MAN

A. C. STEVENSON

Department of Social and Preventive Medicine,
The Queen's University of Belfast, Northern Ireland

This note is concerned with the practical problems that arise in attempting to compare phenotype frequency, gene frequency and mutation rates between different communities. Such a comparison may be desirable for a number of reasons and, indeed, it is always something which is inherently of great interest in human population genetics. In one context, however, the comparisons which have been suggested as particularly desirable are those between communities known to have been exposed to widely different total radiation.

It seems most unlikely that it would be feasible to detect differences of the small order of magnitude which would be expected in such communities, or if they were detected, to attribute them with confidence to differences in background radiation alone. It would appear necessary to elaborate these and other points of criticism, however, because the suggestion has been made so frequently that it is perhaps better not to ignore, but rather to analyse, the difficulties inherent in such comparisons. This must be the writer's excuse if what follows appears largely destructive.

Outline of Problems Involved

The difficulties may be summarized as follows:

1. There are the statistical problems inherent in attempting to detect small differences in very low frequencies based on small numbers, such as mutation rates in man. Suppose in two populations of about 3 000 000 each it was desired to compare the frequency of a dominant or a sex-linked trait with an approximate expected frequency of 1/30 000. Suppose, also, that a background radiation of 3 r per generation to the gonads was expected to cause 10% of all mutations. If the two areas compared had a difference of 4 r in radiation exposure, then it would be necessary to interpret a difference of some 10-20 in the number of affected individuals in the two populations.

2. There are the hazards of assuming that any differences detected in mutation rates between two areas are, in fact, caused by different exposure

to radiation. The proportion of mutations attributable to radiation is not known, and there are other factors—racial, dietary and demographic— each of which separately may determine more variation in rates than that determined by background radiation. The evidence of a close relationship between mutation and parental age is very strong for several of the genes whose expression would be suitable for comparative purposes, so that conventions of age at marriage and of the age interval between the men and women might well greatly influence the mutation rates. There are used in medicine and industry naturally occurring and synthetic substances known to be mutagenic in some lower organisms. Their effects on mammals are unknown.

3. In calculating mutation rates by the indirect method the value adopted for the relative fertility of the specific phenotype could be rather critical. Yet in different populations the actual fertility of the phenotype may vary for social reasons, and because of inadequate or differing sources of demographic information it might be that only a very unsatisfactory method could be used in the comparison of two communities. For example, in Denmark (Mørch [15]) a high proportion of adult achondroplastics have had offspring, while in Northern Ireland at present only one living achondro-plastic is known to have had children (Stevenson [21]). In the State of Michigan, USA, the numbers of offspring born to people of both sexes at different ages can be compared (Falls & Neel [3]), whereas in England and Wales this information is available in respect of females only, and in Northern Ireland there are no national statistics of this kind. Hence the available background demographic information may not be comparable in areas otherwise suitable.

4. An essential for adequate comparison of mutation rates in two communities is that the complete patterns—not the truncated patterns which result from different degrees of ascertainment—should be available. With the best will in the world it is impossible to arrive at complete ascertainment unless the medical services are reasonably well organized, records are good and available, and co-operation is readily given by medical and other authorities. To take a specific example, it is extremely difficult to find the older surviving sporadic boys with Duchenne-type sex-linked muscular dystrophy. If they have not had medical attention for many years, if they only attended a long time previously a hospital which kept poor records, or if they live in an area where the education authorities tend to ignore children who do not attend school, they may be well nigh impossible to find. Any comparisons between communities would therefore need to be supervised by physicians or other persons with plenty of practical experience of the difficulties and of the devices for checking and cross-checking the efficiency of ascertainment.

5. Lastly, there are the dual problems of diagnosis and of the complications introduced when it is appreciated how diverse the apparently

simple relationship between gene and trait usually is. As might be expected from animal work, experience is constantly showing that human syndromes can be determined by genes at various loci or by different alleles. In addition there is, of course, the complication of the occurrence of phenocopies. The more carefully single-gene traits in man are studied, the more complex the picture becomes, so that there is hardly a trait known where there is not either some evidence or a suspicion that the trait may be determined by various mechanisms. This does not by any means depend only on the text-book descriptions of many traits described as being caused sometimes by dominant, sometimes by recessive and sometimes by sex-linked genes. Many of these may well have arisen from the misinterpretation of pedigrees or from the selective publication of the data of remarkable families. However, clinical and biochemical separation of traits and the increasing practice of studying all families with affected members in a community constantly seem to suggest such probabilities. Perhaps more will come to light when more data are available for the analysis of various measurable characteristics of traits, such as measurements between sibs and between all the phenotypes. Perhaps, too, we shall get help in the future from some further knowledge of the morbid anatomy and histology of genetical conditions. The most remarkable example of all is probably hereditary deaf-mutism, where the evidence is strong that many recessive genes and a few dominant ones can each determine deafness which cannot be separated clinically. It is interesting to see that in mice, where similar evidence is available, even histology fails to reveal differences in lesions produced by different genes. In deaf-mutism, too, the so-called "congenital" cases or phenocopies seem to constitute as many as one-third of all cases (Stevenson & Cheeseman [22]).

Such reflections make it difficult to suggest which traits would be suitable for use as markers for comparisons of the kind suggested, and indeed they leave a nasty suspicion in one's mind that certain traits might be chosen as satisfactory largely because not enough is known about them !

Types of Trait Suitable for Use as Markers

It seems worth while here to review briefly the kinds of trait which might be used as markers for mutation rates at specific loci and to point out the practical problems just mentioned as they arise. It will be generally accepted that autosomal-recessive gene traits are quite unsuitable for the purpose. In the first place, they are individually rare. Secondly, variations in inbreeding ratios, difficult to detect except in the crudest form of full-cousin rates in man, together with the fact that if small isolates with close inbreeding produce a number of cases of a rare trait the total rate will be very markedly affected, render it very hazardous to estimate a gene frequency as a preliminary to calculating a mutation rate.

TABLE I. ESTIMATIONS OF MUTATION RATES OF AUTOSOMAL DOMINANT GENE TRAITS

Trait	Basis of estimation of mutation rate	Estimated rate per million	Source
Achondroplasia	Direct : 8 sporadic cases in 94 073 hospital births	43	Mørch [15]
	Indirect: $\mu = \frac{1}{2}(1\text{-}f)x = \frac{1}{2}(1\text{-}0.098) \times \dfrac{86}{3\ 793\ 000}$ (Denmark)	10	
	Direct : 6 sporadic cases in 44 109 hospital births (South Sweden)	68	Böök [2]
	Direct : 9 sporadic cases in 31 753 hospital births	142	Stevenson [21]
	Direct : 37 sporadic cases in 1 387 000 living subjects	13	
	Indirect: $\mu = \frac{1}{2}(1\text{-}f)\,x = \frac{1}{2}(1\text{-}0.09) \times \dfrac{39}{1\ 387\ 000}$ (Northern Ireland)	14	
Epiloia	Direct : Estimated frequency $\dfrac{1}{30\ 000}$, one-quarter of the cases being sporadic (South-east England)	8—12	Gunther & Penrose [8]
Retinoblastoma	Direct : 51 sporadic cases from an estimated number of about 1 500 000 births (London)	17	Philip & Sorsby (unpublished data, 1947)*
	Direct : 49 sporadic cases in 1 054 985 births (State of Michigan, USA)	23	Falls & Neel [3]
	Direct : 47 sporadic cases in 1 376 000 births (Germany)	17 (4)	Vogel [24]

* Based on data of Griffith and Sorsby [7]

TABLE I   (continued)

Trait	Basis of estimation of mutation rate	Estimated rate per million	Source
Waardenburg's syndrome (hair pigment, eye and hearing defects)	Based on proportion of cases observed in deaf mutes, an estimate of "penetrance" and the frequency of deaf mutism (Netherlands)	4	Waardenburg[26]
Multiple polyposis of colon	Based on frequency of condition at autopsy and proportion of cancer of colon autopsies showing some polyposis (State of Michigan, USA)	13	Reed & Neel[7]
Dystrophia myotonica	$\mu = \frac{1}{2}(1\text{-}f)\, x = \frac{1}{2}(1\text{-}^1/_3)\,\dfrac{33}{1\,370\,921}$ (Northern Ireland)	8	Lynas[13]
Marphan's syndrome	$\mu = \frac{1}{2}(1\text{-}f)\, x = \frac{1}{2}(1\text{-}^1/_2)\,\dfrac{36}{1\,370\,921}$ (Northern Ireland)	5	Lynas (unpublished data, 1956)
Aniridia	28 sporadic cases (1875-1944) and 13 isolated cases in 1944 in population of 3 844 000 Estimated frequency $\dfrac{1}{200\,000}$ (Denmark)	5	Møllenbach[14]

In contrast, autosomal-dominant and sex-linked gene traits offer some opportunities for direct estimations and, being less dependent on vagaries from random mating, offer the chance of indirect calculation of mutation rates based on the theoretical distribution of genotypes at equilibrium developed by Haldane.[9]

It may be presumed with some confidence that the genes for which mutation rates have already been estimated are those whose characteristics are most likely to be suitable for comparative purposes. As will be seen from Tables I and II, in which mutation rates for some do minant and sex-linked gene traits are given, the number of adequate calculations made is unfortunately very small and the data from which they are derived are frequently rather meagre or dependent on indirect estimates rather than on actual counts. This is intended not so much as a criticism as an indication of the difficulty—and, at times, impossibility—of assembling data which are sufficient in quantity and quality.

TABLE II.   ESTIMATIONS OF MUTATION RATES OF SEX-LINKED RECESSIVE GENE TRAITS

Trait	Basis of estimation of mutation rate	Estimated rate per million	Source
Haemophilia	Estimates frequency in London as between 35 and 175 per million births and relative fertility of affected male subjects as <0.25 (London)	50	Haldane[9]
	$\mu = \frac{1}{3}(1\text{-}f)\times = \frac{1}{3}(1\text{-}0.286)\times 1.33 \times 10^{-4}$ (Denmark)	32	Andreasson[1] (modified by Haldane[10])
	$\mu = {}^1(/_3 1\text{-}f)x = \frac{1}{3}(1\text{-}0.333)\times \frac{3.163}{4\,092\,025}$ Based on data of Fonio[4] and Andreasson[1] (Switzerland and Denmark)	27	Vogel[25]
Duchenne-type muscular dystrophy	18 cases in 67 000 male live-births $\mu = \frac{1}{3}(1\text{-}f)x = \frac{1}{3}\times 1 \times \frac{18}{67\,000}$ (State of Utah, USA)	95	Stephens & Tyler[18]
	36 cases in 162 448 male live-births $\mu = \frac{1}{3}(1\text{-}f)x = \frac{1}{3}\times 1 \times \frac{36}{162\,448}$ (Northern Ireland)	74	Stevenson[20] (also unpublished data, 1956)
	16 cases in 138 403 male live-births $\mu = \frac{1}{3}(1\text{-}f)x = \frac{1}{3}\times 1 \times \frac{16}{138\,403}$ (England)	39	Walton[27]

Autosomal Dominant Genes

Autosomal dominant genes would seem to offer the best opportunity for collecting data for comparative purposes, and the ideal trait would be one with the following characteristics:

(a) 100% manifestation in the appropriate genotype (this would obviate errors in estimating gene frequency and in identifying new mutant phenotypes);

(b) that only one gene can determine the trait;

(c) that the phenotype cannot be mimicked by a phenocopy;

(d) that the condition is recognizable at birth or in early life but that its possessors do not die too young (this is important, in that otherwise differential mortality experience makes estimates of frequency difficult);

(e) that the frequency of the condition is reasonably high (the lower the frequency, the larger the population which will be needed to detect differences in frequency and, hence, mutation rates);

(f) that selection against the phenotype is marked. (If it is not, direct estimates of mutation rates would be well nigh impossible to obtain as new mutant phenotypes would very seldom be observed. Indirect estimates of the mutation rate would also be less reliable, as unless the diminution of the effective fertility is big enough to be recognized and measured, such estimates could not be made. In a low-frequency trait, with little negative selection, a small number of mutations a few generations previously could result in great differences in phenotype frequency.)

Looking at the traits in Table I and the mutation rates calculated, it is unfortunately easy to point out the deficiencies of each for comparative purposes. Perhaps it may be worth just mentioning them for the benefit of non-medical readers, who may not be familiar with the clinical aspects.

Achondroplasia

There are three certain objections, and another possible one, to the use of achondroplasia as a marker. In the first place, it is fairly clear that achondroplasia as commonly recognized at birth is "different" from achondroplasia as commonly seen in older subjects. Pooling the obstetric history and the foetal condition of Mørch's eight and the writer's nine cases of achondroplasia recognized at birth and born to normal parents (Stevenson[21]), it appears that of the seventeen (six males and eleven females), six were stillborn; eight died shortly after birth; one lived for one year and died of pneumonia; one lived for eighteen months, but never walked or had any teeth, and died of pneumonia; and one lived to twenty-nine years of age. In this last case (one of Mørch's), however, the condition of the father was not known.

Further, in this combined series of cases, six of the mothers had hydramnios in pregnancy and three of the babies had other gross anomalies: one had microphthalmus, heart defect and rudimentary tail, and two had cleft palate, polydactyly and syndactyly.

In Northern Ireland a complete ascertainment has been made of 37 subjects presumed to have received fresh mutations, only three of whom were recognized at birth. All this suggests that the cases recognized in hospital at birth have the type of maternal history and foetal appearance which we usually associate with congenital, but not necessarily hereditary, anomalies. It further raises the question whether the possible survival of mild cases of this type may not complicate the gene frequency and fertility issues in the living. It may also be noted here that it would be hazardous to compare the incidence of this condition in births in various hospitals, as the amount and quality of ante-natal care may alter the incidence. For example, of nine cases born in the Royal Maternity Hospital, Belfast, from 1 January 1938 to 30 June 1956, six mothers were admitted either because of hydramnios or because of pre-natal X-ray diagnosis (four cases).

Secondly, from time to time cases have been reported of two achondroplastic subjects being born to normal parents. Helwig-Larson & Mørch [12] and Grebe [6] have reported such instances, in one of which the parents were cousins. There are two such families in Northern Ireland, and again in one case the parents are full cousins. This suggests that there may be a recessive gene or allele, and introduces another complication.

Thirdly, there are the difficulties of diagnosis. The taller achondroplastic subjects are usually discovered only as the parents of affected children. Several cases about 5 foot in height have been reported. The writer has seen a man 5 foot 1 inch in height, and neither he nor his colleagues can decide whether this man is affected. If he had an affected relative in an appropriate relationship, the issue would probably be beyond doubt.

The separation of achondroplasia from Morquiö's syndrome is perhaps not as easy as is commonly assumed. For example, some cases of achondroplasia seem typical as far as limb-length, shape of head and hands are concerned, yet radiographs of the spine show vertebral changes commonly assumed to be characteristic of Morquiö's disease.

Finally, as already mentioned, in the indirect estimation of the frequency of mutation, the value taken for the relative fertility may greatly alter the figure calculated. In Denmark a very high proportion of subjects have had offspring, mostly illegitimate, whereas only one subject in Northern Ireland is known to have had any children. Thus, variation in social standards would interfere with comparisons.

Epiloia

Epiloia must, it would seem, be ruled out as a marker. The total frequency of the trait as measured is low. Gunther & Penrose [8] estimate 1/120 000 and the nine living cases in Northern Ireland represent essentially the same frequency (Stevenson & Fisher [23]). It is possible to estimate that the real frequency of the genotype is perhaps three times as great, but such speculations, although no doubt valid in some contexts, are hardly satisfactory when attempting to compare two frequencies.

The trouble is that the gene may not be manifested at all or may appear only in such mild or uncharacteristic formation that the condition will not be diagnosed unless attention is called to severely affected relatives. In addition, the condition may be impossible to diagnose before the characteristic skin affections appear, and there will almost certainly be some undetectable cases in any large group of young epileptic children. When one adds that subjects suffer a very high mortality, that relatively few survive for thirty years, and that many cases of tuberose sclerosis are only discovered at post-mortem examination, the difficulties are even more obvious.

Retinoblastoma

This would seem to be a trait more suitable in many ways for the purpose of comparing frequencies, provided that there are good ophthalmological services in the areas observed. Children with eye symptoms rapidly come to the attention of the doctor, and those with the kind of symptoms and signs likely to be caused by retinoblastoma would be referred quickly to an ophthalmologist and the diagnosis would be made, if not immediately, then soon afterwards. In a very high proportion of cases the eyes are enucleated, and histological examination is available to confirm the clinical diagnosis. However, as it seems likely that as many as one-quarter of eyes which are enucleated as a result of retinoblastoma are otherwise affected, biopsy examination is essential.

Falls & Neel,[3] who have made the most complete study as yet carried out, are not willing to exclude the possibility that more than one gene can cause the condition and that some cases, particularly the uni-ocular ones, represent phenocopies. Further, they raise the question of racial differences in frequency by pointing to the apparently low frequency in people of African as opposed to those of European origin. Finally, they were not satisfied that they had made a complete ascertainment.

Waardenburg's syndrome

Waardenburg [26] estimated that the interesting syndrome described by him (hair pigment, eye and hearing defects) had a frequency in the Netherlands of about 1/42 000, but he had to make allowance for an estimated proportion of undiscovered cases. Indeed, a direct estimate would involve examining the whole population for minor signs. It is clear from Waardenburg's account that, in a given subject, only one of the triad of hair anomaly, deafness and eye signs may be present, and it would seem impossible on clinical grounds and in terms of the effort required to examine sufficient people to make a direct estimate of the frequency of the trait. For example, in Northern Ireland only one case has been discovered, and this was a sporadic case which turned up in work on hereditary deafness.

Pelger's leucocyte nuclear anomaly

This appears to be an uncommon trait even in continental Europe, although it is much commoner there than in North America or in the

United Kingdom.[16] Indeed, until controlled studies determine whether these apparent differences are in fact real, and if so whether they are racial or geographic, it would appear rather hazardous to suggest that the trait might be used for the purpose of comparing mutation rates. Further, in the absence of easily recognizable external characteristics it would require examination of perhaps 500 000 samples of blood to find a reasonable number of cases.

Aniridia

The syndrome of aniridia and mental deficiency is estimated by Møllenbach[14] to have a frequency of about 1/100 000. The condition appears to be inherited as a dominant, but with considerable variation down to complete failure of manifestation. The history of some families also suggests that there is a recessive form, and the pattern of aniridia and other associated eye anomalies described within and between families suggests that we may be observing the effects of several different genes or of alternative alleles. It would seem that further studies of this condition are needed before it may be considered for use for our purpose.

Multiple polyposis of colon

A mutation rate for multiple polyposis of the colon was calculated by a most ingenious method by Reed & Neel,[17] but the incidence of the condition could hardly be counted directly. The condition is one of multiple small benign tumours of the colon and rectum, and cases only come to attention (a) when one of the benign tumours undergoes malignant change and causes symptoms, (b) when there is accidental bleeding from the tumours, (c) when the colon is examined by sigmoidoscopy for some other purpose, and (d) when found by chance at autopsy.

These would have to be the starting-points for all cases of ascertainment of sporadic cases and for investigations of families in familial cases. Short of passing protoscopes and sigmoidoscopes on perhaps ten thousand people and chasing relatives with such instruments, it seems unlikely that this condition could be used as a marker !

Dystrophia myotonica

Lynas,[13] in the Department of Social and Preventive Medicine, Queen's University of Belfast, has made the only complete ascertainment of dystrophia myotonica that the writer has been able to discover. The greatest single difficulty in this condition is again failure or partial failure of manifestation of the gene and variation in the age of onset, so that the mildly affected mutant phenotype or the mildly affected members of the present generation of a family could hardly be ascertained. Possibly, very careful assessment of the neurological condition of persons presenting with pre-senile cataract would make it possible to find more cases, but there would still be an element of doubt about many cases.

Marphan's syndrome

Lynas (unpublished data, 1956) has also made a complete ascertainment of Marphan's syndrome. Here again, all the difficulties arise which are inherent in dealing with a trait which is the variable manifestation of an irregular dominant gene. Precisely parallel difficulties to those mentioned for dystrophia myotonica are encountered: diagnostic doubts in mild cases, the impossibility of ascertaining mild cases unless there are more severe cases in the family, and so on.

Sex-linked Genes

Of the sex-linked gene traits, only haemophilia and Duchenne-type muscular dystrophy appear to be sufficiently frequent and well-defined for possible use as markers. The question of differential mutation rates in males and females—raised by Haldane [10, 11] for both these conditions— must be regarded meanwhile as unproven. It should be remembered that we must rely on indirect estimates involving an estimate of relative fertility in calculating rates for sex-linked recessive genes.

Haemophilia

This seems to be a reasonably suitable condition for the purpose, provided that there are adequate clinical pathological facilities for differentiating between haemophilia and allied disorders. Curiously enough, apart from Andreasson's work in Denmark [1] and possibly Fonio's inquiry in Switzerland,[4] no one has made a complete ascertainment of the condition, and with new techniques presenting opportunities of separating out different haemoglobins, such work seems overdue. The increasing life-span and fertility of haemophiliacs make for some difficulty in assessing mutation rates, but these do not seem insurmountable.

Duchenne-type muscular dystrophy

Three complete ascertainments of Duchenne muscular dystrophy have been reported. Stephens & Tyler's [18] and Stevenson's [19, 20] data are strictly comparable clinically, but Walton's [27] include two females and one male who lived to 40 years of age, and who would certainly not be accepted by the other authors. However, the clinical details given by Walton make it possible for the data to be equated, and there is reasonable agreement between the three on gene frequency and mutation rate, though perhaps Walton's ascertainment would seem to be less complete on internal evidence.

Conclusions

To sum up, it would appear unlikely that communities of sufficient size could be found which would have sufficiently different exposures to background radiation to permit detection, far less measurement, of differences in mutation rates.

The basic problem is likely to be statistical. In addition, however, problems in ascertainment, in clinical diagnosis and in the complexity of the underlying genetical mechanisms would add further to the difficulty in using the "single gene traits" which have been suggested as markers.

Finally, since it seems wise not to end on too pessimistic a note, the following points may be worth considering:

1. Suppose the proportion of mutations due to a background radiation of 3 r is not 10% but, say, 20%, the upper limit suggested in the report of the Medical Research Council of Great Britain.[5]   Then given a population of 3 000 000 and a dominant trait with a frequency of about 1/30 000 as before, a difference of just under 5 r near the 3 r level would seem theoretically to give expected differences of the trait of about 30 cases, which might be interpreted as significant. If only 10% of the mutation rate is determined by radiation, then the same numerical difference in cases would require about 9 r difference in background radiation.

2. If, in spite of the difficulties outlined, mutation-rate comparisons are thought to be fundamental, then another type of planned observation than straight comparison between two areas might be more satisfactory. For example, serial comparisons of a number of defined areas, for several traits with carefully planned control of diagnostic standards and ascertainment, and the simultaneous collection of background-radiation information would perhaps be more valuable than a comparison between two areas only.

REFERENCES

1. Andreasson, M. (1943) *Op. dom. Biol. hered. hum. (Kbh.)*, **6**
2. Böök, J. A. (1952) *J. Génét. hum.*, **1**, 24
3. Falls, H. F. & Neel, J. V. (1951) *Arch. Ophthal. (Chicago)*, **46**, 367
4. Fonio, A. (1954) *Die erblichen und sporadichen Blüterstamme der Schweiz*, Basel
5. Great Britain, Medical Research Council (1956) *The hazards to man of nuclear and allied radiations*, London
6. Grebe, H. (1952) *Z. Kinderpsychiat.*, **71**, 437
7. Griffith, A. D. & Sorsby, A. (1944) *Brit. J. Ophthal.* **28**, 279
8. Gunther, M. & Penrose, L. S. (1935) *J. Genet.*, **31**, 413
9. Haldane, J. B. S. (1935) *J. Genet.*, **31**, 317
10. Haldane, J. B. S. (1947) *Ann. Eugen. (Camb.)*, **13**, 262
11. Haldane, J. B. S. (1956) *Ann. hum. Genet.*, **20**, 344

12. Helwig-Larson, H. G. & Mørch, E. T. (1950) *Nord. Med.*, **43**, 180
13. Lynas, M. A. (1956) *Ann. hum. Genet.*, **21** (In press)
14. Møllenbach, C. J. (1947) *Op. dom. Biol. hered. hum. (Kbh.)*, **15**
15. Mørch, E. T. (1941) *Op. dom. Biol. hered. hum. (Kbh.)*, **3**
16. Patau, K. & Nachtsheim, N. (1944) *G/Z. Naturf.*, **1**, 345
17. Reed, T. E. & Neel, J. V. (1955) *Amer. J. hum. Genet.*, **7**, 236
18. Stephens, F. E. & Tyler, F. H. (1951) *Amer. J. hum. Genet.*, **3**, 111
19. Stevenson, A. C. (1953) *Ann. Eugen. (Camb.)*, **18**, 50
20. Stevenson, A. C. (1955) *Ann. hum. Genet.*, **19**, 159
21. Stevenson, A. C. (1957) *Amer J. hum. Genet.*, **9** (In press)
22. Stevenson, A. C. & Cheeseman, E. A. (1956) *Ann. hum. Genet.*, **20**, 177
23. Stevenson, A. C. & Fisher, O. D. (1956) *Brit. J. soc. Med.*, **10**, 134
24. Vogel, F. (1954) *Z. KonstLehre*, **32**, 308
25. Vogel, F. (1955) *Z. ges. Blutforsch.*, **1**, 91
26. Waardenburg, P. J. (1951) *Amer. J. hum. Genet.*, **3**, 195
27. Walton, J. N. (1955) *Ann. hum. Genet.*, **20**, 1

SOME PROBLEMS IN THE ESTIMATION OF SPONTANEOUS MUTATION RATES IN ANIMALS AND MAN *

James V. NEEL

Chairman, Department of Human Genetics,
University of Michigan, Medical School,
Ann Arbor, Mich., USA

In view of the known species differences both in the genetic structure of populations and in the apparent genetic responses to irradiation, when considering the genetic impact of increased exposure to ionizing radiation we should prefer not to attempt to extrapolate from other species to man, but rather to base our thinking entirely on human data. Unfortunately, as has already become abundantly clear, the necessary data on man are not yet to hand, nor is it likely that they will be for some time to come. Under the circumstances, our thinking must for the present be guided to a large extent by what we know about the genetics of other species.

Attempts to quantitate the effects of radiation on human populations have usually been based on five factors. These are:

(*a*) The spontaneous mutation rate/locus/generation.

(*b*) The induced mutation rate/locus/roentgen.

(*c*) The total gene number.[a]

(*d*) The "accumulation factor", i.e., the ratio of nominally recessive genes already present in the population to those arising spontaneously each generation through mutation.

(*e*) The manner in which selection operates on the total gene complex.

Although asked for a contribution on "Extrapolation from animals to man: the problem", this is so very broad an assignment that rather than mention a few generalities about each of the above factors, and how they are manipulated to give estimates of the quantitative risks of radiation, the writer would like to examine in some detail the present state of knowledge as regards just one of them. The factor to be singled out for special

---

* The material presented in this paper is drawn in large part from Chapter XV of a recently published monograph by J. V. Neel and W. J. Schull, entitled " The Effect of Exposure to the Atomic Bombs on Pregnancy Termination in Hiroshima and Nagasaki", and is reproduced by permission of the publishers, the National Academy of Sciences — National Research Council, Washington, D.C., USA.

(*a*) The product of (*a*) $\times$ (*c*), or (*b*) $\times$ (*c*), is the rate of mutation per gamete, spontaneous or induced as the case may be. It is possible in suitably designed experiments to estimate this directly (Muller[15]), and so decrease the number of variables involved in the calculation.

consideration is the spontaneous mutation rate.   There is no deep significance in the choice of this topic, i.e., any one of the four other factors of importance to attempts at extrapolation might almost equally well have been chosen for detailed consideration.   In what follows, attention will repeatedly be drawn to gaps in knowledge.   This should in no way detract from the past accomplishments of investigators in the field, but is submitted in the belief that the primary purpose of this monograph is to review what remains to be done if we are to place in proper perspective the genetic risks of ionizing radiation to human populations.

Current thinking concerning the rate of mutation of mammalian genes is for obvious reasons strongly influenced by what is known concerning rates in *Drosophila*.   No less pertinent, but more difficult to fit into our conceptual framework for man at present, are the extremely important data emerging from the study of other infra-mammalian forms, such as Benzer's recent work on bacteriophage.[2]   We will accordingly first consider briefly what seem to us to be some of the more pertinent data concerning *Drosophila*.   For methodological reasons it is customary to distinguish, on the basis of their physiological effects, between three categories of mutations—namely, those associated with visible effects, those associated with lethal effects, and those which express themselves through a reduction of viability in the absence of detectable somatic effects, the so-called "semi-lethal" mutations (1-10% viability) and "deleterious" mutations (over 10% but less than 100% viability).   Terminology in this field leaves something to be desired.   For example, the "deleterious" mutations must have an organic basis, so that many of them would be found on careful study to be also "visibles".   By the same token, most "visibles" are also "deleterious".   Finally, the dividing line between "lethals" and "semi-lethals" may be altered by culture conditions.   Be that as it may, the division into these three categories has an operational usefulness, as we shall now see.

Beginning with the pioneer attempts of Muller[14] (see also Kerkis[11]) and Timoféeff-Ressovsky,[28] a number of efforts have been made to establish the relative frequencies with which these types of mutations are represented among all mutations.   These attempts have involved radiation-induced rather than spontaneous mutations because of the much more laborious nature of the problem if attacked through the study of spontaneously occurring mutations.   In view of the possibility that the relative frequency of lethals is higher among the radiation-induced mutations because of an increased proportion of minute deletions, the estimate of the ratio, (semi-lethals + deleterious) / lethals, may be a minimum estimate.   Muller[17] (see also Falk[6]) places this ratio at 3-5 to 1.   This same author goes on to state that:

"... the ratio may indeed be considerably higher than this, since the technique was hardly refined enough for the detection of detrimentals with a viability greater than some 85 per cent of normal.   Other studies have shown that 'invisible' mutants causing sterility or lowered fertility of some degree also form a very large group.   This group, however, overlaps, to an extent not yet well investigated, that of the detrimental mutations." [17] (p. 396)

The significance of information concerning the relative frequency of mutants with viability in the 85-99 % range in attempts to quantitate the genetic risks of radiation is of course enormous.   A related problem concerns the frequency of mutations for which the organism *at the time* is able to compensate completely, the undetectable mutations.   Lately, considerable attention has been directed towards the genetic basis and evolutionary implications of physiological homeostasis (see references in Lerner [13]).   The possibility cannot be ruled out that the principle of homeostasis enables some organisms to compensate entirely, under particular sets of circumstances, for the effects of certain mutations.

It may be argued that there is no reason to be concerned about the relative frequency of mutants with undetectable effects in a consideration of the deleterious effects of radiation.   However, these mutations are undetectable only under the conditions set by the observer.   Under other conditions, set by nature and not by man, they might have decided effects. It is not at all difficult to argue that the mutants with over 85 % viability which cannot now be studied in *Drosophila* may in evolutionary importance far outweigh the visibles.

Muller,[16] in a discussion of the question of the numerical relationship between lethals, on the one hand, and semi-lethals and deleterious mutations, on the other hand, has made the following statement:

"However, studies carried on in *Drosophila* during the past year by Meyer, Edmondson, and the writer indicate that in this organism the assumption of an equal distribution of detrimental mutations throughout all i_{ho} values [a] (when represented on an arithmetic scale) does not hold. Instead, it appears that, following the high but descending peak formed by complete lethals ($i_{ho} = 100\%$) and nearly complete lethals (i_{ho} = between 98 % and 100 %), there is a marked drop in the frequency of mutations. The mutations studied were induced in an autosome (the second chromosome) by ultraviolet light acting on an interphase stage (in the polar cap).   Along with 208 complete lethals there were 20 mutants found in the range of i_{ho} between 98 per cent and 100 per cent, and again only 20 in the range of i_{ho} between 90 per cent and 98 per cent, although this range is four times as wide as the preceding one.   If the rest of the distribution, as far as $i_{ho} = 10\%$ had only the same frequency of mutations as in the range between 90 per cent and 98 per cent there would have been only 240 detrimentals in the entire interval between 100 per cent and 10 per cent to set against the 208 complete lethals found.   But since we know from other work, previously cited, that the detrimentals in this interval are in reality several (about five) times as numerous as the complete lethals, it is evident that their frequency must, at lower degrees of detriment (lower i_{ho}), rise very much above that existing in the 90 per cent to 98 per cent range.   The distribution of frequencies of i_{ho} therefore forms a bimodal curve with one peak at the left origin, lethality ($i_{ho} = 100\%$), and another peak somewhere to the right.

---

a) i_{ho} = the amount of impairment produced by a gene when homozygous.

"Little more than this is yet known definitely about the shape of the curve in question, important though this genetic question is. However, there are grounds, both theoretical and observational, for regarding it as very unlikely that the second peak is near the first or that the rise towards it is sharp. Hence it is probable that detrimental mutations, instead of having an even distribution with respect to values of i_{ho}, form a curve which, except for its peak of near-lethals at the left end, is massively skewed towards the right, with its mean at a value of i_{ho} significantly beyond the middle (0.5)."[16] (pp. 140-141)

If we consider these remarks of Muller in conjunction with the possibility of "invisible" mutants discussed earlier, then the problem of estimating the relative frequency of lethal mutants *versus* those viable to some degree assumes new complexity. The figure below attempts to present some of this complexity graphically. The abscissa of this figure represents the viability of the homozygous genotype in some arbitrary environment. In this connexion, it is apparent that the term "lethal" is relative, some lethal mutations having effects under no known circumstances compatible with life, others having far lesser effects. Likewise, the term "normal" as applied to viability is relative, some normals being more normal than others, the differences being brought out only under unusual circumstances. Thus far, observations have been limited to the range of lethality and 1-85% viability. As Muller has pointed out in the statement quoted above, there is great doubt concerning the shape of the curve of numerical relationships within this range. We have indicated two of the principal alternatives. Curve A assumes a mode at 60-70% viability, from which it would seem likely that the proportion of mutations in the 85-100% and normal viability range is small. Curve B assumes that the mode is farther to the right, with the corollary that there is a considerable group of mutations not now being detected. How large that group is depends of course on the shape of the curve.

The question of the relative frequency of lethal mutations as contrasted with visibles is on a somewhat more secure footing than the question of

SCHEMATIC REPRESENTATION OF TWO POSSIBLE "MUTATION SPECTRA"
WITH REFERENCE TO THE DEGREE OF VIABILITY OF THE MUTANT,
BOTH COMPATIBLE WITH THE PRESENT DATA

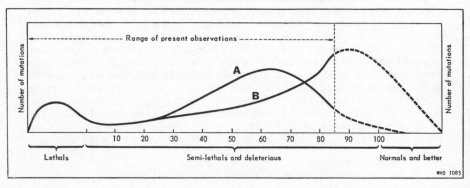

WHO 7083

the ratio of lethal mutations to mutations reducing viability to a lesser degree. In tabulating the results of radiation experiments by five different workers, Schultz [25] found this ratio to be 7.4:1. In view of the well-recognized differences in the ability of individuals to recognize mutant phenotypes, the true ratio is probably somewhat lower. We prefer, for instance, the ratio of 5.2:1, which obtained in the extensive and meticulous experiments of Spencer & Stern. [27] Even this ratio may be too high. For example, in the control cultures, Spencer & Stern obtained a ratio of sex-linked lethals to visibles of 4.3:1 and in the irradiated cultures, a ratio of 5.3:1. In a study on spontaneous mutations in a "high mutation rate" line, the ratio of sex-linked lethals to visibles was 3.6:1 (Neel [21]). The ratio of visibles:lethals:semi-lethals and deleterious mutations may, as an approximation, be said to be somewhere between 1:4:16 and 1:6:30, with, as noted above, the most uncertainty centring about the magnitude of the third figure in the ratio.

The important question of the mutation spectrum at individual loci remains in its early stages because of the amount of labour involved in securing reliable data. The effort involved in studying this problem through the use of spontaneously occurring mutations appears almost prohibitive. Attempts to study the problem using induced mutations again encounter the question of how precisely the mutational spectrum obtained with mutagenic agents parallels that derived from the study of spontaneous mutations. However, there is some preliminary evidence that the ratios just given may vary significantly from locus to locus. Thus, although there are many instances of lethal and visible mutations arising at the same locus, there are also a few cases in which a locus does not appear to be essential to life, in the sense that flies with a deficiency for this locus may live although they are of reduced viability (e.g., yellow and achaete, Muller [15]). These loci, then, would not produce at least one type of lethal mutation. Finally, for methodological reasons, localizing "deleterious" mutations to specific loci is extremely difficult, so that studies relating these to the loci producing lethals and visibles are in an early stage.

It should also be pointed out that the question of the total relative frequency of mutation at different loci is in a very unsettled state. Although there seems no doubt that the rate of recovery of mutations differs from locus to locus, care must be exercised in reasoning as to the magnitude of the true differences (Neel & Schull [23]). In the following discussion of mutation rates at specific loci, the fact that these are *selected* loci must constantly be borne in mind.

With respect to the rate of occurrence of spontaneous "visible" mutations at specific loci in *Drosophila*, data are available from five extensive series of observations. These are summarized in Table I. Space does not permit the writer to give this table the detailed attention it deserves. In most of these studies, some special circumstance occurred that requires at least very brief mention.   Thus, Muller, Valencia & Valencia [19] observed in other experiments with the same strain used for their "visible" mutation series that the rate of occurrence of sex-linked lethal mutations in this strain was 0.7%, a rate some fourfold greater than usual.   From this they argue that "the frequency of gene mutations at the nine loci would *ordinarily* average between 10^{-5} and 7×10^{-6} per locus in females" [19] (p. 125). However, in view of the possibility that these "high mutation rate" lines contribute significantly in nature to the total of spontaneous mutation (Ives;[10] see also Neel [21]), it seems appropriate simply to average this finding with the others.   From the data of Glass & Ritterhoff, [7] it would appear that the mutation rates of males are higher than those of females, but this is scarcely substantiated by the difference in the findings of Alexander [1] and Muller, Valencia & Valencia. [19]   Accordingly, we have simply averaged all the findings without regard to sex.   No attempt has been made to take into account the effect on the observed results of possible differences in the age of the flies tested.   The paper of Glass & Ritterhoff contains additional data on mutation rates emerging incidentally to their study, but it has seemed preferable in this summary to utilize only data on loci "pre-selected" for mutation rate estimates.   It would appear that Muller and his colleagues, and Schalet (unpublished data), did not score as mutants flies with mutant phenotypes which were infertile, whereas Glass & Ritterhoff did.   In any mutation rate study, a considerable proportion of apparent mutants prove sterile.   Schalet encountered one "cluster" of ten "cut" mutants, presumably due to a mutation occurring in a spermatogonium. One can argue as to whether this should be scored as 1 or 10 mutations in the context of the present discussion.   Finally, in all these studies where mutation gives rise to one mutant in a culture of wild type, there is the question, probably not so serious in studies on man, of the extent to which the less vigorous mutants are eliminated prior to the inspection of the culture, and the further problem of the human factor in recognizing the mutant.

While, then, it is possible to "correct" the data of Table I in several ways, the writer has made no attempt to do so.   In a total of 4 625 945 locus tests, at least 41 mutations were recovered, a rate of 0.9×10^{-5}. However, *this applies only to "visible" mutations, or to lethal and deleterious mutations which in combination with a mutant allele have visible effects.* If other lethals, semi-lethals, and deleterious mutations are arising at these same loci which are without detectable visible effects with the test-crosses employed, the mutation rate must be higher.   There is no way at present to estimate the amount of mutation not detected with current specific locus techniques, but if, for instance, the ratio of visibles: (undetected lethal + semi-lethal + deleterious + sterile mutations) at these loci were as high as 1:4, the mutation rate per locus becomes 4×10^{-5}.   In other words, there are some grounds for feeling that the commonly quoted mutation

TABLE I. FREQUENCY OF OCCURRENCE OF SPONTANEOUS "VISIBLE" MUTATIONS IN VARIOUS SPECIES

Author	Chromosome	Number of organisms	Number of loci	Total locus tests	Mutations	μ
Drosophila:						
Muller, Valencia & Valencia [19]	X (females)	±60 000	9	540 000	15	2.8×10^{-5}
Altenburg, after Muller et al. [19]	X (females)	±50 000	8	400 000	0	0
Alexander [1]	III (males)	45 504	8	364 032	0	0
Glass & Ritterhoff [7]	multiple (females)	100 414	4	401 656	1	2.5×10^{-6}
	multiple (males)	102 759	4 (1 sex-linked)	359 657	17	4.7×10^{-5}
Schalet (unpublished data)	X (males)	111 600	14	1 562 400	6*	0.4×10^{-5}
	X (females)	71 300	14	998 200	2	0.2×10^{-5}
				4 625 945	41	0.9×10^{-5}
House mouse:						
Russell [24]	several	37 868	7	265 076	2	0.8×10^{-5}

* One of these mutants appeared as a "cluster" of 10 flies. If one is concerned only with the rate of recovery of mutant phenotypes, then the entry here should be 15, and the average of the five studies quoted becomes 1.1×10^{-4}.

rates for specific loci for *Drosophila* are conservative. If, on the other hand, the mutation spectrum at specific loci is restricted, as some evidence suggests it to be (see p. 143), in the sense that some loci give rise predominantly to "visibles" and others to "deleterious" mutations, then the "true" mutation rate may be closer to the 1×10^{-5} which emerges from specific locus studies than to the 4×10^{-5} suggested above.

Two other studies involving individual loci should be quoted. Lefevre, [12] in a paper which contains an excellent discussion of the problem of estimating spontaneous mutation rates, reports that the rate of appearance of mutants with visible or lethal effects at the *y* locus is "about 1 per 75 000" (p. 379). On the other hand, Bonnier & Lüning, [3] in a paper criticized by Muller [17] because the rate of recovery of spontaneous mutations appeared to be too low in comparison with certain other findings, observed only one mutation at the white and forked loci among 153 579 flies tested for visible mutations, a rate of 0.3×10^{-5}. Again, neither of these estimates takes into account the semi-lethal and deleterious mutations which may not be detected by the techniques being employed.

TABLE II. ESTIMATED AVERAGE MUTATION RATES PER LETHAL-PRODUCING LOCUS IN SEVERAL DROSOPHILA SPECIES [*]

Species	Second chromosome	Third chromosome
D. melanogaster	1.1×10^{-5}	. . . . .
D. pseudo-obscura	. . . . .	1.1×10^{-5}
D. willistoni	2.2×10^{-5}	3.0×10^{-5}
D. prosaltans	1.1×10^{-5}	2.1×10^{-5}

[*] After Dobzhansky, Spassky and Spassky [4]; these investigators considered their estimates more likely to be overestimates than underestimates.

Utilizing a somewhat different approach, Dobzhansky, Spassky & Spassky [4] have estimated the average rate of mutation to lethals, semi-lethals (1-20 % viability), and visibles *per lethal-producing locus* in different species. These estimates, which the authors felt were more likely to be overestimates than underestimates, are reproduced in Table II. Again, the estimate does not include the deleterious mutants.

In summary, then, it would appear that depending on one's view of the representativeness of the loci studied, and of the problem of the relative frequency of mutations not detected by current techniques, there is room for a divergence of opinion concerning the average rate of mutation of *Drosophila* genes, with the range of possibilities perhaps extending from 0.5×10^{-5} to 5×10^{-5}. In our opinion, even this range of estimates must be applied with great caution to human problems.

Turning now to mammals, we find that significant studies are available for only two species, the house mouse and man himself. The figures for the house mouse were derived in much the same fashion as the figures quoted for *Drosophila*—namely, through a search for mutant individuals among animals simultaneously heterozygous at multiple loci. Russell, [24] in connexion with his important observations on radiation-induced mutations in the house mouse, found that in his control material the rate of appearance of *visible* mutations in 265 076 locus tests was 0.8×10^{-5}. The observational error is, of course, large. Again it must be recognized that such tests very probably detect only a fraction of the mutations occurring at these loci.

There seems no reason to labour further the point that our knowledge of spontaneous mutation rates at specific loci is poor for any species. In some attempts to extrapolate from non-human material to man, the additional problem arises of the greater life-span of man than of laboratory material, as well as the question of the type of species which man represents in terms of mutation rate. While the writer would be the first to defend the animal work as providing the best estimates available at the present time, it is his opinion that, in the final analysis, figures for man himself must be obtained.

The available estimates for the frequency of occurrence in man of certain mutations with visible effects are summarized in this publication by Professor A. C. Stevenson and Professor L. S. Penrose. [a] Many of the problems involved in estimating human mutation rates are discussed by these two authors, and since they have also been dealt with previously (Haldane; [8,9] Neel; [22] Neel & Schull; [23] Nachtsheim [20]), they will not be re-examined here. The average of the available estimates of the rate of mutation for the autosomal dominant and recessive sex-linked mutations thus far investigated in man is in the neighbourhood of 2×10^{-5} / locus / generation. These estimates, now, are entirely limited to mutations with visible effects. Because of the nature of the design of observations on human mutation rates, it seems possible that a higher proportion of the mutations at the specific loci being studied is going undetected in man than in *Drosophila*. There is no way of estimating the magnitude of this difference at present, but a total mutation rate as high as 1×10^{-4} at these loci is a possibility. Although the apparent correspondence between human and *Drosophila melanogaster* rates is noteworthy, because of the differences in the way the rates are obtained one must be cautious in the emphasis placed on the similarity. However, if the correspondence were indeed valid, this has interesting implications concerning the importance of "aging" and failures in the "copying process" at mitosis, and the role of background radiation, in spontaneous mutation rates.

---

a) See articles on pages 125 and 101, respectively.

The representativeness of these estimates for man has been repeatedly challenged. There can be no doubt that there is definite selection in the loci studied. How this influences our estimates is not at all clear. As has been pointed out elsewhere (Neel & Schull [23]), mutation at any particular locus may be thought of in terms of these aspects: (a) the frequency of mutation at that locus; (b) the number of alternative forms of the gene which may occur at any locus, i.e., the number of multiple alleles; and (c) the ease with which the effect associated with each of these multiple alleles can be detected. We assume that some loci are more mutable than others because we detect the results of mutation more frequently at these loci. However, making allowance for "unstable" loci, the hypothesis has not been disproved that the inherent instability of all the genes is, by virtue of their biochemical complexity, very similar, but that the results of mutation are more readily detected at some loci than at others because of the role of that particular locus in the animal's physiology. It is entirely conceivable that the loci [a] thus far selected for study in man are those at which a high proportion of all possible alleles results in readily detectable effects, but at which the per locus mutation rate is fairly representative of the human species.

For purposes of calculation, estimates of the rate of mutation of human genes have included 10^{-5} (Evans [5]), 10^{-7} (Wright [29]), and 2×10^{-5} (Muller; [16] Slatis [26]). In the current state of our knowledge, students of the problem can select and justify estimates differing from one another by a factor of 100.

If space permitted, we would do well to submit to the same kind of scrutiny our knowledge concerning the other factors that enter into quantitative treatments of the risks of irradiation: namely, induced mutation rates at specific loci; gene number (or, alternatively, gamete mutation rates); the accumulation factor; and the mode of action of selection. But it is obviously impossible to do so here. In closing, though, the writer would like to say just a few words about the nature of selection in human populations. To begin with, there would seem to be little problem in extrapolating from animals to man, since there is practically nothing known concerning the detailed action of selection in animal populations on which to base an extrapolation. For all our allegiance to the principle of natural selection, it is amazing how little we know of its actual detailed workings. True, it is easily demonstrated in experimental populations that grossly defective individuals seldom reproduce. But the problem of how the population as a whole maintains its fitness is virtually untouched. To mention only one important point, to what extent does the stability and adaptability of the species rest on the mechanism of balanced

---

a) In point of fact, we do not know that any particular mutation rate study in man is not detecting mutation at several loci.

polymorphism, a mechanism not readily disturbed by an increase in mutation rates?

There is one final point the writer would like to emphasize. In attempts to evaluate the genetic risks of increased radiation to the human species, he is a strong proponent of extensive animal experimentation. Through such work, possibilities can be explored which would either involve prohibitive amounts of time or be impossible for man. But when differences do appear between two animal species, as is already the case, only work on man will tell which of the species he resembles more closely. It is of tremendous significance to the practice of medicine and the development of atomic energy whether the "permissible" population dose above background is 3 r or 30 r per generation. Before reaching any final conclusions concerning permissible radiation doses in man, regardless of what is learned concerning other animal species, we must accumulate far, far more data on man himself than are now available.

REFERENCES

1. Alexander, M. L. (1954) *Genetics*, **39**, 409
2. Benzer, S. (1955) *Proc. nat. Acad. Sci. (Wash.)*, **41**, 344
3. Bonnier, G. & Lüning, K. G. (1949) *Hereditas (Lund)*, **35**, 163
4. Dobzhansky, Th., Spassky, B. & Spassky, N. (1952) *Genetics*, **37**, 650
5. Evans, R. D. (1949) *Science*, **109**, 299
6. Falk, R. (1955) *Hereditas (Lund)*, **41**, 259
7. Glass, B. & Ritterhoff, R. K. (1956) *Science*, **124**, 314
8. Haldane, J. B. S. (1948) *Proc. roy. Soc. B.*, **135**, 147
9. Haldane, J. B. S. (1949) *Hereditas (Lund)*, **35**, Suppl., p. 267
10. Ives, P. T. (1950) *Evolution*, **4**, 236
11. Kerkis, J. J. (1935) *The preponderance of "physiological mutations"*. In: *Summary of communications presented at the Fifteenth International Physiological Congress*, Leningrad-Moscow, p. 198 (Quoted by Muller [14])
12. Lefevre, G., jr (1955) *Genetics*, **40**, 374
13. Lerner, I. M. (1955) *Amer. Nat.*, **89**, 29
14. Muller, H. J. (1934) *Radiation genetics*. In: *Proceedings of the Fourth International Congress of Radiology*, Zürich, vol. 2, p. 100
15. Muller, H. J. (1935) *J. Hered.*, **26**, 469
16. Muller, H. J. (1950) *Amer. J. hum. Genet.*, **2**, 111
17. Muller, H. J. (1954) *The nature of the genetic effects produced by radiation*. In: Hollaender, A., ed., *Radiation biology*, New York, vol. 1, p. 351
18. Muller, H. J. (1955) *Bull. atom. Scient.*, **11**, 329
19. Muller, H. J., Valencia, J. I. & Valencia, R. M. (1950) *Genetics*, **35**, 125
20. Nachtsheim, H. (1954) *Naturwissenschaften*, **17**, 385
21. Neel, J. V. (1942) *Genetics*, **27**, 519
22. Neel, J. V. (1952) *Amer. Nat.*, **86**, 129
23. Neel, J. V. & Schull, W. J. (1954) *Human heredity*, Chicago
24. Russell, W. L. (1954) *Genetic effects of radiation in mammals*. In: Hollaender, A., ed., *Radiation biology*, New York, vol. 1, p. 825

25. Schultz, J. (1936) *Radiation and the study of mutations in animals.* In: Duggar, B. M., ed., *Biological effects of radiation*, New York, vol. 2, p. 1209
26. Slatis, H. M. (1955) *Science*, **121**, 817
27. Spencer, W. P. & Stern, C. (1948) *Genetics*, **33**, 43
28. Timoféeff-Ressovsky, N. W. (1935) *Nachr. Ges. wiss. Göttingen (Math.-physik. Klasse, Fachgruppen VI. Biol.)*, **1**, 163
29. Wright, S. (1950) *J. cell. comp. Physiol.*, **35**, Suppl. 1, p. 187

EFFECT OF INBREEDING LEVELS OF POPULATIONS ON INCIDENCE OF HEREDITARY TRAITS DUE TO INDUCED RECESSIVE MUTATIONS

N. FREIRE-MAIA

Director, Laboratory of Genetics, University of Paraná,
Curitiba, Paraná, Brazil

It is well known that the incidence of hereditary traits in populations depends not only on the respective gene frequencies, but also on the breeding structure of the populations. One of the important aspects of the prevailing mating pattern can be measured through the use of the coefficient of inbreeding, a population parameter practically impossible to evaluate in natural populations of animal species, but very easily determined in man.

Inbreeding in Brazil

During the past six years, the writer has become very interested in this particular problem in human genetics and has tried to discover the inbreeding levels under which the present-day Brazilian populations live, as well as the magnitude of the same parameter during the last 150 years. The study of this problem in Brazil is greatly facilitated by the fact that much data can be obtained through the analysis of Catholic marriage records, a source of information which is available for the great majority of the population. The calculation of the coefficients of inbreeding has been done on the basis of data on the frequencies of marriages between uncles and nieces, aunts and nephews, first cousins, first cousins once removed, and second cousins. A few of the results obtained have already been published (Freire-Maia [2, 3, 4]), but the great bulk of the data will be presented in a paper now in preparation.

The following features of the breeding pattern of Brazilian populations have become apparent:

1. The degrees of inbreeding vary greatly in different regions: the rates are relatively low in the south and in parts of the east (a mean level of about 1% of first-cousin marriages has been found); are very high in in large regions of the east and north-east (a level as high as 10% for first-cousin marriages has been detected); and are intermediate, but highly variable, in other regions.

2. There is, in general, a clear trend towards decreasing inbreeding rates, although a few reversals of this trend have been noted.

3. Geographic inbreeding gradients have been detected in some zones, with increasing inbreeding from the coast to the hinterland.

4. Although some of the Brazilian rates of inbreeding are higher than the highest so far found in other countries, the mean Brazilian coefficient of inbreeding (0.002) is relatively low because about one-third of the population lives at the level of 1% of first-cousin marriages.

An analysis of the factors probably responsible for the different degrees of inbreeding found in Brazil revealed that cultural pattern, economic level, migration, population density and degree of ruralization seem to be the most important.

Effect of Inbreeding on Population Structure

It is known from theoretical analysis that inbreeding coefficients as high as 0.01 and 0.02, such as are found in some localities, produce negligible effects on common recessive traits, but have a considerable influence on the rare ones (Table I). Suffice it to say, for instance, that characteristics

TABLE I. EFFECT OF TWO COEFFICIENTS OF INBREEDING (0.01 AND 0.02) ON INCIDENCE OF RECESSIVE TRAITS WITH DIFFERENT GENE FREQUENCIES (q)

$q\%$	$q^2\%$	$\alpha = 0.01$			$\alpha = 0.02$		
		$\alpha pq\%$	$q^2 + \alpha pq(\%)$	$\frac{\alpha pq}{q^2}(\%)$	$\alpha pq\%$	$q^2 + \alpha pq(\%)$	$\frac{\alpha pq}{q^2}(\%)$
50	25	0.25	25.25	1	0.5	25.5	2
20	4	0.16	4.16	4	0.3	4.32	8
10	1	0.09	1.09	9	0.18	1.18	18
5	0.25	0.0475	0.2975	19	0.095	0.345	38
1	0.01	0.0099	0.0199	99	0.0198	0.0298	198
0.5	0.0025	0.004975	0.007475	199	0.00995	0.01245	398
0.1	0.0001	0.000999	0.001099	999	0.001998	0.002098	1998

with a gene frequency of 1% will, under the action of a coefficient of inbreeding of 0.01 (which prevails in large populations in Brazil), have phenotype frequencies 99% greater than those expected in a model assuming no inbreeding (Table I) and 90% greater than those expected in populations with a coefficient of inbreeding of 0.001 (Table II). These almost 100% increases could hardly be detected in a direct way, through the analysis of the phenotype distribution in the populations, but may be appreciated through the incidence of the so-called "recessive" diseases in the offspring

TABLE II.   EFFECT OF TWO COEFFICIENTS OF INBREEDING (0.001 AND 0.01) ON INCIDENCE
OF RECESSIVE TRAITS DUE TO GENES WITH FREQUENCY OF 1%

Incidence of the traits		Increment
$\alpha = 0.001$	$\alpha' = 0.01$	$\dfrac{\alpha' pq}{q^2 + \alpha pq}$
0.01099 %	0.0199 %	90 %

of consanguineous marriages, as well as through the incidence of consanguineous marriages among the parents of people presenting the same kind of genetic traits.   Some data obtained on deaf-mutism show, for instance, a really very high inbreeding effect.   In a population where the frequency of first-cousin marriages has been estimated as 3.5%, there has been shown to be about 21% of first-cousin marriages among the parents of deaf-mute children (Aguiar & Freire-Maia [1] and unpublished data).   Inasmuch as some of these children undoubtedly owe their defect to extrinsic factors, the frequency of consanguinity among the parents of children with genetically determined defect is of course even higher. This problem will, however, be discussed in detail elsewhere.

Effect of Inbreeding under Increased Mutation Rate

In recent times one of the most important human genetics problems is the evaluation, on a quantitative basis, of the effects of increasing radiation levels on the genetic composition of populations.   Unfortunately, no accurate mathematical treatment could be given to this subject up to the present, as no precise information has yet been collected on some basic phenomena—namely, the spontaneous mutation rates, the induced mutation rate per gene per roentgen, the total number of loci, etc. (see discussion in Neel & Schull [9]).   Thus the treatment to be presented below is *not* intended to show what happens under increasing radiation, but what could happen under increasing inbreeding.   The emphasis will be put *not* on the rates of mutation frequency increment but rather on the fact that, assuming a given increment, the action of different inbreeding rates will produce different quantitative effects.

For instance, assuming that the probability of induced mutation per gene per roentgen in man is of the same order (2.5×10^{-7}) as that found in the mouse (Russell [10]), doses of 100 r would increase this probability to 2.5×10^{-5}.   Thus, five different populations (A, B, C, D and E), differing only in the intensity of inbreeding, with two given recessive genes at frequencies of 0.007 and 0.003, will have the frequencies of these genes increased respectively to 0.007025 and 0.003025. However, the increase of the frequencies of the recessive genotypes will depend on the inbreeding level of each population (Table III). Five inbreeding coefficients have been chosen for comparison: 0.001, 0.003, 0.006, 0.009 and 0.011. The first one, representative of European populations according to Haldane, [6]

TABLE III. EFFECT OF INBREEDING LEVEL OF POPULATIONS ON FREQUENCY OF RECESSIVE TRAITS UNDER INCREASED MUTATION PRESSURE, ACCORDING TO HALDANE'S FORMULAE [6] [*]

Population	Coefficient of inbreeding (α)	Initial frequency of recessives $q^2 + \alpha q(1\text{-}q)$ (A)	Increment of recessives $\triangle q(\alpha+2q)$ (B)	Increased frequency of recessives (A+B)	"Total" increment [**] (B × 30 000)
$q = 0.003$ $q+\triangle q=0.003025$					
A	0.001	0.000011991	0.000000175	0.000012166	0.00525
B	0.003	0.000014973	0.000000225	0.000015198	0.00675
C	0.006	0.000026946	0.000000300	0.000027246	0.00900
D	0.009	0.000035916	0.000000375	0.000036291	0.01125
E	0.011	0.000041901	0.000000425	0.000042326	0.01275
$q = 0.007$ $q+\triangle q=0.007025$					
A	0.001	0.000055951	0.000000375	0.000056326	0.01125
B	0.003	0.000069853	0.000000425	0.000070278	0.01275
C	0.006	0.000090706	0.000000500	0.000091206	0.01500
D	0.009	0.000111559	0.000000575	0.000112134	0.01725
E	0.011	0.000125461	0.000000625	0.000126086	0.01875

[*] For details, see Neel et al. [8]
[**] Assuming an identical behaviour of 30 000 loci in gametes (Spuhler [11])

also holds true for southern Brazil; the third has been assumed to characterize the highly inbred Japanese populations as a whole (Neel et al. [8]); the fourth is the highest detected Brazilian coefficient for a large zone (the centre of the north-eastern region); the fifth is probably the coefficient now prevalent in the populations of the last-mentioned zone; and the second has been selected to represent an intermediate step between the "low" European level (0.001) and the "high" Japanese one (0.006). Table III shows how much different coefficients of inbreeding may change the phenotype composition of populations subjected to the same radiation impact. With the initial frequency of 0.003, it is seen that the Brazilian coefficients 0.009 and 0.011 produce total increments (0.01125 and 0.01275) more than twice as great as that produced by the European and southern Brazilian coefficient of 0.001. With the initial frequency of 0.007, the effect is a little smaller. The action of the Japanese mean coefficient is somewhat intermediate, as expected. Other things being equal, then, it is to be expected that induced recessive mutations manifest their effects with much higher frequencies in populations with inbreeding rates like those found in some Brazilian regions than in some European or North American populations.

Prospective Genetic Research on Inbreeding

Now that we possess the basic information on inbreeding rates in Brazil, it has been possible to discover some "modern" populations living at inbreeding levels probably comparable to those of European communities in the Middle Ages. In the focus of the highest inbreeding levels in Brazil, for instance, some localities have been found where as many as 1 out of 6 and 1 out of 5 of the marriages are contracted between first cousins, and 1 out of every 3 marriages is consanguineous up to and including second cousins. This situation would seem to be of great potential usefulness in the study of the general effect of consanguineous marriages on the genetic make-up of populations and the discovery of the mean number of deleterious recessive genes per individual. Unfortunately, in the zones in Brazil where the very high inbreeding rates prevail, no analysis regarding the incidence of specific hereditary anomalies seems feasible because the level of medical practice there is lower than in the larger cities. Nevertheless, in these regions a study can be made of such population characteristics as the frequencies of abortion, miscarriage, stillbirth, infant mortality, malformations as a whole, etc., and should afford some interesting results. Furthermore, in Rio de Janeiro, São Paulo, and some other cities, where the inbreeding rates are probably from ten to twenty times higher than those prevailing in similar or even smaller cities in the USA (Glass;[5] Herndon & Kerley;[7] Steinberg (cited by Woolf et al.[12]); Woolf et al.[12]), and where very good hospitals exist, a complete and detailed analysis is possible.

ACKNOWLEDGEMENT

The writer is indebted to Dr J. V. Neel and Dr J. N. Spuhler for discussions in connexion with the preparation of this manuscript.

REFERENCES

1. Aguiar, W. C. & Freire-Maia, N. (1953) *Ciênc. e Cult.*, **5**, 203
2. Freire-Maia, N. (1952) *Amer. J. hum. Genet.*, **4**, 194
3. Freire-Maia, N. (1953) *Ciência*, **1**, 26
4. Freire-Maia, N. (1954) *Coefficient of inbreeding in some Brazilian populations.* In: *Proceedings of the Ninth International Congress of Genetics (Caryologia (Torino)*, Suppl.), p. 923

5. Glass, B. (1950) *Cold Spr. Harb. Symp. quant. Biol.*, **15**, 22
6. Haldane, J. B. S. (1947) *Ann. Eugen. (Camb.)*, **14**, 35
7. Herndon, C. N. & Kerley, E. R. (1952) *Cousin marriage rates in Western North Carolina* (Paper presented at the annual meeting of the American Society of Human Genetics, Ithaca, N.Y.; unpublished)
8. Neel, J. V. et al. (1949) *Amer. J. hum. Genet.*, **1**, 156
9. Neel, J. V. & Schull, W. J. (1956) *The effect of exposure to the atomic bombs on pregnancy termination in Hiroshima and Nagasaki*, Washington, D.C.
10. Russell, W. L. (1952) *Cold Spr. Harb. Symp. quant. Biol.*, **16**, 327
11. Spuhler, J. N. (1948) *Science*, **108**, 279
12. Woolf, C. M. et al. (1957) *Amer. J. hum. Genet.*, **9** *(In press)*

———

DETECTION OF GENETIC TRENDS IN PUBLIC HEALTH

Howard B. NEWCOMBE

*Biology Branch, Atomic Energy of Canada Limited,
Chalk River, Ontario, Canada*

To assess the practical genetic consequences of irradiating human populations, one must either: (*a*) extrapolate from mutation-rate studies in exposed animals, or men, to the effects of the additional mutations on human health and fitness; (*b*) extrapolate from fitness studies in animals to health and fitness in man; or (*c*) measure the important changes in the genetic component of health and fitness directly in the human populations which are exposed to a rising background of radiation.

The first two of these approaches have received considerable emphasis because the experimental procedures are relatively straightforward, and because predictions are needed, however tentative they may be. Unfortunately, however, it is extremely difficult to extrapolate from increase in mutation rates to the magnitude of the resulting increases in amount of general ill-health, or from the fitness of animal populations to the fitness of human populations. In fact, there is reason to doubt whether the extent of the effect of a given increase in background radiation can ever be adequately anticipated.

The logical complement to prediction lies in the development of some sensitive means of detecting important genetic trends before they have gone too far. Ultimately, of course, this detection is the only way our predictions can be tested.

The main deterrents to setting up a continuing survey aimed specifically at the detection of important long-term genetic trends are the absence of any certainty as to how sensitive a method can be devised, and the very considerable financial and organizational difficulties. However, since we lack the assurance that "prediction" alone will fill our needs, it seems important that the feasibility of "early detection" should receive much fuller consideration than it has in the past.

The present account deals with the application of certain of the methods of vital statistics to such detection. It seems essential to make it quite clear that the suggestions which follow are not at present recommended lines of action for general adoption by central vital statistical or record departments.   These suggestions have been made earlier within Canada, solely as personal recommendations, with a view to studying their feasibility. As presented here, however, the remarks are designed simply to show the possibility of collecting specific data on human variation which could not possibly be assembled on a comparable scale by the conventional *ad hoc* field inquiries used in population genetics.   The methodology is discussed in this paper in the hope of getting constructive criticism before we embark on research on such a large scale.

Sources of Information

In general, to discriminate between genetic and environmental causes (either in genetic conditions of individuals or in population trends) information is needed concerning the numbers of affected and unaffected individuals, their family relationships, and the environments to which they have been exposed.   Considerable information of all three kinds exists in the routine registrations of births, deaths and marriages.   The handling procedures are not at present designed to discriminate between the genetic and environmental contributions to the diseases which are reported on the death registrations, but if maximum use were made of all three kinds of information we could presumably make such a distinction with at least some degree of success.

Since routine vital statistics are a recognized measure of the health of a population, one approach to the detection of genetic trends would seem to lie in supplementing the basic information where necessary, and in designing handling procedures to distinguish the genetic from the environmental causes of ill-health.

The approach is limited at present with regard to the health information, which relates solely to causes of death and stillbirth, but other routine sources could be tapped.   For example, one Canadian province (British Columbia) has made use of the "Physician's Notices of Births and Stillbirths", which are quite separate from the birth registrations, to obtain details of stillbirths and congenital abnormalities.   The problem of adequate ascertainment is undoubtedly soluble.

The chief advantage in the use of registrations of births, deaths and marriages, however, is that these contain, in raw form, the most reliable and complete information on the family relationships of the individuals who make up the population.   They are in essence a family tree on a very large scale (complete with marriage dates, birth dates, and the dates of all deaths).   To extract this family information manually, and to convert it into a usable form, would be a prodigious task, and for this reason we have concentrated much of our thinking on the development of mechanical procedures involving the matching and sorting of punch cards to form a "Family Register Index".

FIG. 1. FAMILY REGISTER INDEX: PROCEDURE FOR IDENTIFYING BROTHER-SISTER GROUPS

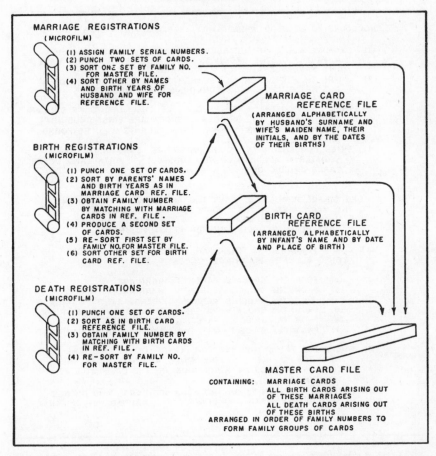

If both the family information and the vital statistics are included on a single card, tabulations from the Master Card File will yield family sizes and numbers of children "affected", from which sibling correlations can be derived. Note that with the use of a miniature card the storage space required for the Master Card File would be about the same as that needed for the microfilms of the corresponding registration forms.

A "Family Register" would contain cards for all marriages, starting from a given year. To these would be added the cards for all births arising out of these marriages, which would be identified and sorted into their respective sibling groups. In addition, all cards for stillbirths and for the deaths of offspring would be similarly identified and sorted. A further procedure has been devised whereby any marriages between first cousins could be identified, together with the births and deaths of their offspring,

FIG. 2. FAMILY REGISTER INDEX: PROCEDURES FOR IDENTIFYING
FIRST-COUSIN MARRIAGES

A   PROCEDURE TO BE USED WHEN FAMILY INDEX IS FIRST STARTED.

    (1)   EXAMINE ALL MARRIAGE REGISTRATIONS FOR CASES IN WHICH
A PARENT OF THE GROOM AND A PARENT OF THE BRIDE HAVE
THE SAME SURNAME (OR MAIDEN NAME).

    (2)   WHERE THIS IS OBSERVED, SEARCH THE BIRTH RECORDS OF
THE BRIDE AND GROOM FOR THE BIRTH YEARS OF THE
PARENTS OF SIMILAR NAME.

    (3)   THEN, SEARCH THE BIRTH RECORDS OF THE PARENTS OF SIMILAR
NAME. WHERE THE BRIDE AND GROOM ARE FIRST COUSINS
THE NAMES OF THE COMMON GRANDPARENTS WILL BE FOUND
ON BOTH REGISTRATIONS.

    (4)   ENTER CONSANGUINITY ON THE MARRIAGE CARD IN THE FAMILY
REGISTER INDEX, AND ON ALL SUBSEQUENT BIRTH AND DEATH
CARDS ARISING OUT OF THIS MARRIAGE.

B.   A MORE DIRECT PROCEDURE USING THE FAMILY NUMBERS ASSIGNED
TO THE MARRIAGES IN THE TWO PRECEDING GENERATIONS
(THE METHOD WILL BE USABLE AFTER THE FAMILY REGISTER
INDEX HAS BEEN IN OPERATION FOR ABOUT 40 YEARS).

    (1)   CARRY FORWARD THE FOLLOWING FAMILY SERIAL NUMBERS
ONTO ALL NEW MARRIAGE CARDS:

      (a)   FROM THE GROOM'S PARENTS' MARRIAGE
      (b)   FROM THE BRIDE'S PARENTS' MARRIAGE
      (c)   FROM THE GROOM'S PATERNAL GRANDPARENTS' MARRIAGE
      (d)   FROM THE GROOM'S MATERNAL GRANDPARENTS' MARRIAGE
      (e)   FROM THE BRIDE'S PATERNAL GRANDPARENTS' MARRIAGE
      (f)   FROM THE BRIDE'S MATERNAL GRANDPARENTS' MARRIAGE

    (2)   WHERE THE FAMILY NUMBER FOR (c) OR (d) IS THE SAME AS
THAT FOR (e) OR (f), THE BRIDE AND GROOM ARE FIRST
COUSINS. CARDS IN WHICH THIS IS THE CASE WILL BE
IDENTIFIED MECHANICALLY.

    (3)   ENTER CONSANGUINITY ON THE MARRIAGE CARD, AND ON ALL
SUBSEQUENT BIRTH AND DEATH CARDS ARISING OUT OF THE
MARRIAGE.

The first of these procedures can be used immediately in the case of all provinces where the maiden names of the mothers of both bride and groom appear on the marriage registration form (i.e., all provinces in Canada except Quebec).

The second procedure will enable consanguinity data to be obtained from all of the provinces, after the Family Register Index has been in operation for a sufficient period.

without resorting to interviews and without reference to any other kind of record (see Fig. 1 and 2).

Thus, for each disease condition on which information is available, it would be possible to determine the incidence within three groups of individuals: the population as a whole, the offspring of first-cousin marriages, and the siblings of affected individuals. This seemed the most suitable use to make of the family relationship data in an initial study, but the information could be applied in many other ways.

In addition, the registrations contain a considerable amount of routinely recorded information on environment, which would permit a breakdown of any data by the following factors: rural or urban residence; socio-economic class, as derived from father's occupation; age of mother and of father at time of birth; family size and spacing; racial origin; gestation period; legitimacy or illigetimacy; and home *versus* institution birth. This is probably adequate for any initial study, and supplementary information could undoubtedly be obtained.

The "Family Register Index" is the one unique feature of the present proposals. In emphasizing the mechanical methods involved, it should be explained that it was felt that the personal-interview technique of obtaining pedigrees would become too laborious in any study involving both a large population and many of the common diseases. And yet, if the common diseases were not included, or if the study were limited to a few genetically simple "indicator conditions", it would be difficult to relate any trend observed to the general health of the population. And the latter is, of course, our ultimate practical concern.

In making these proposals it has been assumed that the present problem of genetic damage from radiation, and the related problem of the operation of other causes in the production of genetic trends, are of sufficient importance to justify any appropriate changes in the collection and analysis of statistics relating to the health of the whole population. Our prime concern is with broad categories of ill-health, and methods of obtaining and handling information on the very large numbers of affected individuals and their relatives need to be developed.

Rationale

In general, the greater the complexity of the genetic and the environmental causes of a condition, the more information of the three kinds (i.e., pertaining to health, family and environment) will be required to disentangle the two.

Thus, to look for a trend in the frequency of a simple dominant "indicator" condition, it would only be necessary to observe the proportions of affected individuals in the population. And to detect trends involving a simple recessive gene it would be sufficient to know the proportions of affected individuals in offspring from consanguineous parents. However, if one extends the survey to conditions arising from a recessive gene with incomplete penetrance, it would be necessary, in addition, to know the corresponding proportion of affected individuals in the rest of the population. In this case the gene frequency would be calculated from the ratio of the two, referred to as a "K" value; and since penetrance affects both components of the ratio equally, both "K" and the calculated gene frequency would be essentially independent of penetrance.

The number of diseases can, of course, be extended still further to include those due to dominant genes of unknown penetrance and those due to multiple additive genes, using comparisons between siblings (or other closely related individuals). Formulae for the estimation of gene frequencies from data of this kind (using the ratio of the incidence in close relatives of affected individuals to that in the population as a whole, i.e., a "K" value) have been derived by Penrose [1] and applied to a number of common diseases.

Where our main interest is in the detection of changes in the gene frequencies, rather than in the absolute frequencies, the problem is considerably simplified. Attention centres on trends in the values of "K", and it is not essential to know whether the genes are recessive, dominant, or multiple additive.

Thus, a basic requirement for discriminating between the genetic and the environmental trends affecting public health is a knowledge of the proportions of affected individuals within three groups of people: the offspring of consanguineous unions, the close relatives of affected individuals, and the population from which these were drawn.

Sources of Bias

Environmental changes, when they affect penetrance uniformly throughout the population, are unlikely to produce spurious trends in the estimates of gene frequencies. This is true also of changes affecting the extent of the ascertainment, and of changes in diagnostic fashion, when they occur uniformly throughout the population. However, there are a number of sources of error, and additional information would be needed in order to detect and evaluate them. Such information would relate mainly to the environment.

Gene frequencies based on consanguinity data would be least subject to bias, the main source of which is the fact that marriages between close relatives tend to be more common in certain sectors of the population—notably, the rural groups. To eliminate errors from this source it would be necessary to obtain independent values of "K" from the various population groups (e.g., breaking the data down by: rural or urban residence; racial origin; socio-economic class; etc.) or, better still, from comparisons with offspring from the brothers and sisters of the individuals who married their cousins.

Gene frequencies based on "K" values for sibling comparisons may be biased in a number of ways. In general, where there are family-to-family differences in environment affecting the expression or penetrance of an hereditary disease, the increased tendency for affected individuals to appear within particular families will increase the value of "K" and bias the estimate of gene frequency downwards. Environmental heterogeneities which might give rise to this kind of bias could be associated with:

(*a*) maternal effects due to the mother's hereditary constitution; (*b*) maternal effects due to the environment to which the mother has been exposed; and (*c*) effects due to the child's post-natal environment. It should be possible to detect any bias from these sources, and to estimate its magnitude.

Thus, where there are maternal effects due to the mother's heredity, these should make for a closer resemblance between the children and any of their first cousins by their mother's sisters, than with first cousins of the other three kinds (i.e., offspring of the mother's brothers, of the father's sisters, or of the father's brothers). The extent of the discrepancy (allowance having been made for differences in the likelihood of inheriting similar X-chromosomes) should indicate the magnitude of the bias. Important environmental variables other than inherited maternal effects should be strongly correlated with the incidence of the condition in a suitable breakdown by environmental groups.

Environmental differences may operate by altering either the expression of a genetic condition (i.e., the "penetrance" or "expressivity") or the production of non-genetic effects which simulate the genetic condition (i.e., "mimics" or "phenocopies"). Variations in environment might tend to group the affected individuals into families by either mechanism, thus increasing the value of "K" and causing the gene frequency to be underestimated. But variations in the production of mimics could operate in the opposite manner through obscuring the grouping due to genetic causes. Both environmental influences will be observed in an appropriate breakdown of the data, as a correlation between environmental group and incidence of affected individuals.

The two effects will in many cases be distinguishable, however, by observing the "K" values for appropriate environmental groups. Where the influence is on penetrance, the value of "K" for any homogeneous group will tend to be less than that for the mixed population (and the estimates of gene frequency will be less biased). Where the influence is on mimic production, the value of "K" for a genetic condition would tend to be increased in homogeneous favourable groups where mimics are rare, and decreased in the unfavourable groups where they are common. In either case, the most reliable estimates of gene frequency would be obtained from groups living in the most uniformly favourable environments.

Such refinements, using information which is already collected as a matter of routine, would remove many of the sources of bias. Further, since genetic applications were not envisaged in the planning of the present systems of vital statistics collection, improvements could undoubtedly be devised after any major attempt to apply the existing information. It is, of course, impossible to predict just how sensitive a means for the detection of genetic trends might eventually be developed; this can only be done as experience is gained in using the information which we already have in a readily available form.

In case the present proposals seem over-optimistic, it is worth noting that at least one serious attempt has already been made to detect a genetic trend in a complex quantitative character (namely, intelligence [2]) which is known to be subject to environmental influences, and that this attempt has made very little use of information on family relationships and environment, and of the refinements which these permit.

Details of Facilities and Procedures

Microfilms of the registration forms for all births, deaths and marriages occurring in Canada are kept centrally at the Bureau of Statistics. From each of these microfilms, a punch-card, bearing a non-repetitive serial number and containing particulars of the event and of the individuals involved, is prepared as a matter of routine. At present a modification in the punching of these cards is under consideration. The modification is designed to enable each birth card to be identified mechanically with the marriage card of the parents, matching by name of father, maiden name of mother, and parents' initials and birth years; while the death cards would in a similar manner be identified with the individuals' birth cards, matching by family name, first name and initials, province and date of birth. A small proportion of apparent discrepancies are known to arise, almost all of which could be matched manually.

The new birth and death cards would have additional blank spaces into which could be transferred the serial number from the corresponding marriage card. This operation would be mechanical, and the serial number from the marriage card would then become a "family number", enabling all three cards to be readily identified into family groups.

The change in the method of punching would not add appreciably to the present costs, which are in the vicinity of $100 000 per year, while the additional matching procedures and the punching of the family number might perhaps double these costs. This estimate refers to a proposed ten-year pilot study, but in a continuing study the handling of an expanding file of cards would involve a further increase in cost which has not as yet been estimated.

In addition, to identify all marriages between first cousins, the microfilms of the marriage registration forms would be scrutinized, and those in which one of the bride's parents had the same family name as one of the groom's parents would be singled out. In the case of these registrations (which amount to about 1%-2% of all marriages in Canada), the birth records of the bride and groom, and then of the respective parents of similar family name, would be checked for positive identification of the marriages which are in fact between first cousins. One man can scan approximately 1000 marriage registrations a day for this purpose, and searching of birth records is a function which the provinces carry out routinely at a relatively small cost.

When a Family Register Index is created, it would be used in conjunction with an Ill-health Register of all "affected" persons, who will be identifiable by their names and by the dates and places of their births, if they have not already been identified by the "family number". The latter register would include stillbirths, infant deaths, other deaths, congenital malformations, hospital records, other medical records, etc. From the two registers one would derive the sizes of the sibling groups and the numbers of affected individuals in each. Weinberg's propositus method would be used to calculate the probability that a sibling of an affected individual will be similarly affected: $p = \Sigma\, x\,(x - 1)\,/\,\Sigma\, x\,(s - 1)$, where p is the required probability, x the number of affected persons in the families, and s the number of children of the individual families. The incidence of the condition in the offspring of first-cousin marriages, and in the population as a whole, would be obtained directly.

The Family Register Index can be thought of as a major research tool, designed to do away with the need for obtaining pedigrees by personal interview and thus to pave the way for whole-population studies of common diseases. Such studies would seem to be an integral part of any attempt to measure the practical consequences of genetic trends in terms of the as a general health of the population.

Details of Suggested Ten-Year Pilot Study

It has been proposed that before embarking on a major continuing programme of an entirely new kind, the design should be tested in a preliminary special study. In the present case there is an additional reason for such a study.

The main programme, if started solely with current registrations of marriages, and of the births and deaths of the children arising out of these, would require approximately four years before any comparisons could be made in brother-sister groups, and about ten years before it would have expanded sufficiently to yield data for a breakdown by cause of death. Only then would it be possible to evaluate the design of the project.

To avoid loss of time a special study could be carried out, essentially similar to the projected continuing study, but using existing records on a "backlog" basis. In drawing up the specifications it was assumed that the special study would cover the ten-year period from 1946 to 1955 inclusive. An attempt has been made to foresee the amount and kind of data which might be expected from the special study. It is estimated that there would be in the vicinity of a million infants born to the marriages under study, and that approximately half of these would have at least one brother or sister with whom comparisons could be made.

The special study would deal mainly with infant deaths, and should indicate the extent to which deaths from various causes tend to be correlated in families and in the offspring of first-cousin marriages. These correlations (i.e., the factors by which the various causes are more common in these two groups of individuals than in the population as a whole) are the values which will be expected to change with changes in gene frequencies. The study would show how large these factors are for the various causes of death, together with the confidence limits, and would at the same time indicate any changes which should perhaps be made in the design of the continuing study.

In addition, since the relatives of affected individuals constitute a group in which the frequencies of the predisposing genes are, as it were, artificially increased, the results should give us a better appreciation of the practical consequences of an increase in the incidence of deleterious genes in the population as a whole.

The extensive Family Register Index, developed during the special study, would be used in the continuing study so that current births from much earlier marriages could be included from the start. This would ensure an appreciable annual yield of data without having to wait until the marriages occurring in the first year of the study had yielded two children.

Future Facilities and Their Potentialities

With the present punch-card equipment a storage problem would eventually develop. The Family Register Index must contain three cards for each individual who has been born, married and died, and family groups of cards will have to be retained until the last of the brothers and sisters has died. Probably the equilibrium number of cards would be in the vicinity of three for each living member of the population. The obvious solution is a system of miniature cards, capable of being mechanically sorted and matched. If, in addition, these cards had an increased information capacity and could be handled more rapidly, the usefulness of the Family Register Index would be enormously increased.

One such system — the Kodak Minicard, which has been described by Tyler, Myers & Kuipers [3]—is in the process of development. (Details: card size, 32 mm by 16 mm; storage space required, 15 inches by 30 inches by 50 inches per 2 000 000 cards; digital information capacity, between five and six times that of the standard punch-cards, with room for a photographic image of the original registration form as well; handling speeds of 1800 cards per minute for sorting and selecting.) Such a medium could replace both the existing microfilm and the punch-cards, while taking approximately the same space as the microfilm alone.

The most important use for the additional information capacity would be in the identification of relatives more distant than brothers and sisters. The "family identity number" assigned at the time of marriage would be carried forward, not only to the children's birth and death cards, but to the children's marriage cards as well, and so on. The number of steps in this carry-over would of course depend ultimately on the amount of digital information space allocated to ancestor-family numbers.

Let us assume, for example, that two generations of ancestor-family numbers are present on all cards (requiring, for 10-digit numbers, 60 out of the 420 spaces which will be available when the card contains a photographic image as well). Causes of death could then be compared in children, parents and grandparents, and in other relatives as remote as second cousins, using a single sorting and matching of death cards.

Another medium which might have applications is magnetic tape. (Information capacity, 100 characters per inch; handling speed for tabulation and other purposes, 15 000 characters per second.) Records from cards which had been suitably sorted in advance could be incorporated each year, together with the accumulated records of previous years, into a single master-tape, which would be revised annually. Assuming that such a tape contained records from 50 000 000 cards with 100 characters per card, it would require approximately 100 hours (not counting the changing of reels) to run the entire tape through a machine in order to tabulate the information in the required form.

In view of the rapid improvement in the designs of such equipment, the bulk of information to be processed, and the complexity of the operations involved, should not constitute more than a temporary limitation on any system of handling which was deemed necessary.

Conclusion

In this account it has been assumed that we may not be able to assess adequately the genetic damage occurring in irradiated human populations, either from a knowledge of the changes in mutation rates, or by observing the changes in fitness in similarly irradiated animal populations, or even by observing the prevalence of a number of genetically well-defined "indicator conditions". With each of these observations there remains an uncertainty as to the amount by which the ill-health of the population has been altered, and if the answer cannot be stated in such terms it is of only limited use.

This would seem to lead us to the much more arduous and exacting task of attempting to detect changes in the genetic factors which affect broad categories of human ill-health. The degree of precision which might be achieved is impossible to predict, but it is clear that we could not afford to waste any of the available information relating to the health of the individuals who make up the population, to their family relationships, or to the environments in which they have been reared.

Experience in effectively handling the masses of information of these three kinds which are at present readily available would seem to be one of our immediate needs, while improvement in the routine sources of information is another. It is with the first of these needs that the present paper has been primarily concerned.

ACKNOWLEDGEMENTS

While the opinions expressed in this paper are entirely those of the writer, the procedures described are the outcome of numerous discussions with representatives of the Bureau of Statistics and the Department of National Health and Welfare, and with other geneticists. In the latter connexion, the writer would like to thank Mr Fraser Harris, Mr S. J. Axford, Mr Gordon H. Josie, Dr A. P. James and Dr F. Clarke Fraser for their generous co-operation.

REFERENCES

1. Penrose, L. S. (1953) *Acta Genet. (Basel)*, **4**, 257
2. Scottish Council for Research in Education (1949) *Report of the...*, London
3. Tyler, A. W., Myers, W. L. & Kuipers, J. W. (1955) *Amer. Documentation*, **6**, 18

POSTSCRIPT

The above account deals with a particular long-term genetic application of information from vital records. The techniques described have other possible uses of a more short-term nature in the study of the genetics of whole populations. These include: (*a*) almost any type of pedigree study; (*b*) consanguineous marriage studies; (*c*) twin studies, which make use of the fact that approximately half of the twin pairs of like sex are genetically identical; (*d*) maternal and paternal age studies; and (*e*) differential fertility studies.

Since the above paper was written a need has become apparent for information on possible differentials of fertility in the relatives of individuals afflicted with serious hereditary diseases. Estimates of the possible magnitude of the radiation hazard based on the present incidence of genetic defects involve an assumption that the mutation rates are instrumental in keeping the genes in the population in spite of a selection against them. It is conceivable, however, that favourable differentials of reproduction in the heterozygotes are more common than is generally believed. Direct evidence on this point is needed, but such evidence will be obtainable only if reproductive potentials of the order of 1% or so can be detected, and for such a purpose limited *ad hoc* studies are almost certainly too insensitive. Procedures for obtaining the masses of information inherent in the routine vital registrations therefore offer what is probably the only means of arriving at such direct evidence.

H. B. NEWCOMBE
24 April 1957